695

ROOKIE CATCHER
with the Atlanta Braves

SPORTS BOOKS BY C. PAUL JACKSON

For younger boys

CHRIS PLAYS SMALL FRY FOOTBALL
FULLBACK IN THE LARGE FRY LEAGUE
LITTLE LEAGUE TOURNAMENT
LITTLE MAJOR LEAGUER
PEE WEE COOK OF THE MIDGET LEAGUE
TOMMY, SOAP BOX DERBY CHAMPION
TWO BOYS AND A SOAP BOX DERBY

For older boys and men

HIGHSCHOOL SPORTS

BUD BAKER PLAYS JUNIOR HIGH BASKETBALL
BUD BAKER PLAYS JUNIOR HIGH FOOTBALL
BUD BAKER PLAYS SENIOR HIGH BASKETBALL
BUD BAKER, RACING SWIMMER
BUD BAKER T QUARTERBACK
FULLBACK IN THE LARGE FRY LEAGUE
JUNIOR HIGH FREESTYLE SWIMMER

PROFESSIONAL SPORTS

BULLPEN BARGAIN
MINOR LEAGUE SHORTSTOP
PRO FOOTBALL ROOKIE
PRO HOCKEY COMEBACK
SUPER MODIFIED DRIVER
WORLD SERIES ROOKIE

ROOKIE CATCHER with the ATLANTA BRAVES

by C. PAUL JACKSON

Illustrated by Francis Chauncy

HASTINGS HOUSE, PUBLISHERS • New York

For JIM FANNING,
giver of a lot of help for this book.

Copyright © 1966 by C. P. & O. B. Jackson, Inc.

All rights reserved. No part of this book
may be reproduced without
written permission of the publisher.

Published simultaneously in Canada
by Saunders, of Toronto, Ltd., Toronto 2B.

Library of Congress Catalog Card Number: 66–11901

Printed in the United States of America

CONTENTS

PART ONE

From Factory Team to Winter Instructional League

1: A Surprised Boy

HE STOOD IN THE batter's box on the third base side of the plate. The bat looked smaller than it was in the grip of his big hands. He wriggled wide, thick shoulders and settled his spikes in the dirt. He swung the bat twice.

"Man out there at the pickup station, Zeke!" The coach at third base clapped his hands. "We gotta have this run, pick him up!"

Teammates on the bench yelled. "Make 'im get that thing in there, then pickle it, Big Man! . . . Take this chucker apart right now, Zeke-boy! . . . Put the wood to it, kid!"

"Knock me around, Zeke!" The baserunner at second pleaded. "You can hit this guy, the old confidence!"

Zeke Pender was aware of the shouts. He always had confidence when he was at bat. It was other things than hitting that threw him. He forced his mind back to the business at hand and concentrated on the pitcher.

This lefthander had got him out three times. What difference that each time he had hit the ball hard, straight at some fielder? The leftie had shown he clearly believed he could get Zeke Pender out again.

"Percentage baseball might dictate that the clean-up hitter be walked, with first base open." His manager had called Zeke from the on-deck circle to tell him this after the man batting ahead of him doubled. "At least give you nothing good to hit at. But an intentional walk would put the go-ahead run on base. This guy's cool and smart. You're up there at the dish this time on your own. Watch it!"

The southpaw slipped two pitches through the strike zone and put Zeke in a hole. But the youngster refused to go after teasing pitches out of the strike zone. Now, with the count three-and-two, the cagey pitcher still could keep the ball off the plate.

He won't, Zeke thought. *Not with two out. He figures he's got my number. He'll blaze his best fireball in there for an out pitch!*

The lefthander delivered. It was his fast ball, just a little high. Zeke gauged the pitch even as his reflexes brought the bat around in a smooth, level swing.

Crack!

Seasoned ash met speeding horsehide. The ball was a murky white streak off the bat. Three feet above the shortstop's glove as he leaped high, the drive was still rising when the sphere disappeared over the fence to the right of the 390-feet marker in left center field.

The bench emptied. Teammates crowded around Zeke as he stepped on the plate after rounding the bases. They grasped his hands, pummeled his ribs, slapped his back. After he had reached the bench, a player stitting next to Zeke said, "Come up with pokes like that game-winner next week and you'll have scouts swarming around you like hungry bees!"

Zeke gave the other a look, shook his head.

"Scouts, s-c-o-u-t-s," the teammates said. "Guys beating the bushes hunting for baseball talent to feed major league outfits. If you think there won't be dozens of big league scouts at the American Baseball Congress national tournament, you have seven more thinks coming! And the ABC tourney is where the winner of this game will go, big boy!"

"I was shaking my head at that game-winner crack," Zeke said. "They still have their ninth inning coming up, you know."

"Yeah, but we aren't through with ours. That wrong-hander out there gets upset when he's tagged for a really long hit. We're liable to grab a flock of runs. But yours will still be the game-winning blow. You're on the way to a convention of big league scouts, Zeke-boy!"

The southpaw broke off a change-up curve that fooled the batter. His easy popup was smothered by the third baseman. Three outs. The wrong-hander apparently was not very upset after all.

Zeke could not honestly say he hadn't thought about the American Baseball Congress national tournament as he left the dugout. His team held a 4-3 lead, and he was glad that prospects for a trip to the ABC tourney were good. Several of his teammates had legitimate hopes of attracting attention from pro scouts.

Not Zeke Pender.

"Let's face it, boy." The manager of the factory league club had pulled no punches with Zeke when the team was being shaped. "You fancy yourself as a catcher: you'd never make a good receiver. You're slow and awkward, and the pitchers wouldn't have confidence in you. Also, we've got two experienced catchers. Your chances of making the club as a catcher would be mighty slim.

"You do hit a ball a country mile when you connect, and we can use a long-ball bat. Be content to play right field and you'll make the club. You can help yourself at the plant, get a better job and more dough, by playing ball. But forget catching."

Zeke sighed as he trotted to his position in right field. The coach of the only other team he had played for—a Little League team, five years ago—had never said anything about awkwardness. Maybe because Zeke Pender had been the only kid who wanted to catch. It could be that if a fellow had been able to go to high school, coaching would have developed him into a catcher. Could be?

The big rightfielder pushed everything from his mind but the job of getting the next three of the rival team out. The top of their batting order would come to the plate.

Loss of the umpire's call on a three-and-two pitch to the leadoff batter did not appear to trouble the pitcher of Zeke's team too much. Tying run on first, clearly a bunt situation.

The batter missed a bunt attempt. He jabbed an

outside pitch foul. Then he swung feebly at a breaking ball that fooled him badly and struck out. The likelihood of a bunt decreased. But the batter striding to the plate was the home club's long-ball hitter. A sharp "downer" to the slugger broke into the dirt and eluded the catcher. The baserunner sped to second. First base open, the potential tying run at the pickup station—a decision faced Zeke's manager.

Putting the potential winning run on base might be questionable strategy. On the other hand, the slugger was not very fast. To put him on base would set up a possible double play from a ground ball.

Zeke saw the sign flashed from the bench. They were giving the long-ball hitter an intentional walk. The cleanup man, the surest hitter on the opposing club, swung bats in the on-deck circle, then stepped into the batter's box.

He was a righthanded batter. He had hit to the left each of three previous times at bat. Outfielders shifted to the left. The batter swung at the first pitch, and Zeke Pender's heart came up into his throat. A roar rose from the fans. The ball was well hit, but a little too far out in front, over the fence—five feet foul.

"Keep it away from him! Pitch him outside. Another fat one like that and he'll break up the ballgame!"

Zeke yelled the words, although he knew they could not be heard by the pitcher above the din of the crowd. Zeke edged two steps farther toward center field. The pitcher broke a curve wide and away. Ball one. Another breaking pitch was too low. Ball two. His fourth offering sizzled through the outside edge of the strike zone. Two-and-two.

Then it happened.

A good pitch, breaking away from the batter, was very close to the strike zone. The hitter had to protect the plate. He swung—really more poked—at the two-and-two curve. The ball slanted off the bat toward right field. It was a line hit, not a weak blooper.

Zeke Pender started with the sound of bat meeting horsehide. He raced all out, knew as he drove himself that more than ordinary speed was needed to reach the ball before it fell safely.

He also knew the agonizing truth that his slowness was far below ordinary speed.

Zeke did not come within three yards of the ball. It ricocheted off the fence and bounded around in the right field corner.

The tying run scored from second. The man who had been intentionally walked raced toward third while the batter chugged around first and then returned to the bag. Zeke caught up with the ball, whirled and put everything he had behind a peg to the plate.

Only a strong arm could have made that throw. The ball sped straight and true, in the air until about even with the pitcher's mound, but it was all in vain. The winning run crossed the plate before the ball bounced off the turf and into the catcher's mitt.

Champions of their local recreation leagues, a good ballclub, the team that had been practically on the way to the American Baseball Congress national tournament had now finished their season.

Because they had a fellow in right field running slower than molasses at the North Pole, Zeke thought. *I'd better quit trying to play ball anywhere!*

He noticed the tanned man in street clothing who stood near the bus into which disconsolate players were climbing. The trip to their motel was apt to be gloomy, not to mention the long ride home. Zeke was caught entirely off balance when the tanned man stepped forward and confronted him.

"Just a minute, Pender," he said. "My name's Naffing, Bob Naffing. This isn't the place for the kind of conversation we're going to have. But I want to be sure you don't do anything with anyone else before we *have* the conversation."

Zeke looked at the man blankly. *He must be some kind of a nut,* he thought.

Naffing did not look like an odd-ball. He was an inch or two shorter than Zeke's six-three and probably twenty pounds lighter than the boy's one-ninety-five. His eyes were about the same shade of brown and his hair nearly as dark as Zeke's, but a lot thinner. Zeke was further puzzled by a haunted feeling that he should know who this man was. He shook his head.

"You must have the wrong fellow," Zeke said.

"Huh-uh. You're the guy who poled a tape-measure-type homer in the ninth."

"And lost the ballgame because he ran too long in one place!" Zeke's reply was grim. "What could anyone want to talk to me about?"

"It was a wrong-field blow that any outfielder would have been lucky to reach." Naffing's tone brushed away the thing that was so painfully in Zeke's thoughts. "Forget it. You're the man I want to talk with, all right. You're Claude Harold "Zeke" Pender. You'll be nineteen years old next May. You quit school after finishing eight grades and didn't play high school ball and that explains why we had only the sketchiest book on you. Answer just one question before we go on: has the class you would have been in been graduated from high school?"

Zeke was still puzzled. "My class was graduated a year ago last June," he said.

"That's what I figured, but I had to be sure. The Commissioner's office strictly enforces baseball's rule against approaching a boy before his class has been graduated."

"I didn't finish high school, but I don't think I'm a stupe." Zeke frowned. "I've read about high school players being followed by big league scouts. You must have something to do with a pro outfit. But you're talking to the wrong fellow, or something's bad wrong somewhere."

"Huh-uh. Everything's on the up-and-up. You were on our list submitted to the Commissioner's office. I work for the Atlanta Braves organization. I'll drive you to your motel, wait for you to shower and change, and we'll have dinner and talk."

Naffing chuckled, then added: "I talk better after wrapping myself around a steak. I hope it won't take too much talk to sell you on playing ball in the Atlanta Braves system."

Zeke swallowed a dryness in his throat. There had to be some mistake. Scouts for big league clubs did not sign a fellow who had just lost an important game for his club, who had definitely shown that his manager's opinion about being slow and awkward was all too valid.

"I just don't get it." The husky youth shook his

head. "You have to be kidding. I could never make it in fast company as an outfielder."

"That could be debatable, Pender. There are men drawing big league checks who aren't much faster than you, if any. But, frankly, the Braves wouldn't be interested in you as a prospective outfielder. We want to develop you as a catcher."

Zeke jerked a startled gaze at him, and Naffing held up a hand.

"A lot of ballplayers make it in pro ranks at positions different from those they think they should play. Hold off whatever you were going to say until we talk. Deal?"

Zeke nodded dazedly. He said through incredulous surprise, "Deal. I'll probably break all records for showering and changing!"

2 : You Can't Stay Awed

THEY HAD FINISHED dinner. Zeke hadn't planned anything of the sort, but he was saying things that had been bottled up in his thoughts. He finished by telling Naffing what the manager of the factory team had said about his catching ambitions.

"That may explain why he's managing a factory league club instead of a pro club," Naffing said. "A special kind of judgment is needed to evaluate raw baseball talent—and even then a man misses.

"But your manager can blow a judgment of a young player and nothing much happens. It's usually costly to a major league organization. Oh, it's true we spend large sums of money on busts. Then sometimes our 'busts' come back to haunt us with another club. We take every precaution and go along with kids, and if we get a few ballplayers who can help us, we're happy."

The man on special assignment for the Atlanta Braves regarded Zeke a moment, then he said, "A boy has to have some natural athletic ability, but the biggest thing he can have going for him is desire. Does he *want* to play professional ball? Just how much? Enough to work, and *work* and WORK?"

Zeke Pender did not answer immediately. His tone was earnest when he spoke.

"It's more than wanting to play ball with me, Mr. Naffing. I don't think anyone could have more desire. Nobody would work harder to make it. But I just can't afford to go off half-cocked and leave my job, even for a contract with a professional club."

Bob Naffing nodded. "We learn all we can about a boy before we talk contract," he said. "We know that you support your mother. You left school when your father was crippled in an accident and needed your help on the farm. We know that he died about a year ago, and after paying funeral expenses and outstanding obligations, there was no farm left. You took a job at the plant where you're still working. We know how much money you make and the prospects for promotion. I wouldn't attempt to talk you into leaving the security a steady job provides if I didn't honestly believe you have much better prospects with us."

Zeke stared at the man. Naffing seemed to divine the questions that filled Zeke's thoughts.

"Baseball scouting is far-reaching and thorough," Naffing said. "A card was turned in by somebody about a kid playing Little League ball who hit with power and did a fair job of catching. His name was Pender, and he was called Zeke probably because he was a farm boy. Reports on youngsters just don't stop with Little League unless there's a negative notation. Nothing negative had been added to your card.

"Our Scouting Director got in touch with our scout for this area, and he dug out the reason why your baseball career seemed to end with Little League. Then he found out you were playing factory league ball. He watched you in a half-dozen games and reported that you had power at the plate, a fine arm, and excellent attitude. I suppose it was because I caught during my active baseball career that they sent me to look you over."

Something clicked in the back of Zeke's mind. He said, almost as though talking to himself, "Bob Naffing, a great catcher for the Braves. That's why I thought I should know you. You look different in street clothes. I had your picture on a bubble gum card years ago when I used to dream of some day catching for a big league club."

"Your dream could come true, Zeke. In looking at prospects for professional baseball, a boy who can hit must be signed. If he has arm-strength and reasonable agility, we can teach him to catch. If he will work, he will learn to catch and receive, and they're two distinct abilities. You can hit; that peg from deep right field had to be from arm-strength, and you say you're willing to work."

Naffing drew folded papers from his pocket. "I think you'll find the terms of this contract attractive," he said. "Your mother will have to sign with you, since you're a minor. We can't offer you the bonus that we paid Manley—a mistake, in my judgment—but this amount will be paid you immediately on receipt of the signed contract in our Atlanta office." He penciled a figure in the margin of the contract. "It's more than ample to see your mother cared for until you begin receiving paychecks next spring."

Zeke looked at the figure, glanced at the contract, and nodded. He said, "It's more money per year than I make at the plant, and I can keep my job until late winter, anyway."

"No. A clause has been typed at the end of the standard form. It's for your benefit. You'll report to the Braves' office in Municipal Stadium, West Palm Beach, Florida, as soon as you can wind things up here and get down there. You will be paid $350 a month as a member of our Braves in the Florida East Coast Winter Instructional League."

Naffing arose, extended his hand. "It's in your lap, Zeke," he said. "I have to make a stop at Waycross, Georgia, regarding our farm club training site there, but I'll be in West Palm before the guys report. I'll see you there?"

"You'll see me there." Zeke nodded. "Mom'll be tickled to sign the contract with me, I know."

Zeke Pender was awed by the first sight he had of West Palm Beach Municipal Stadium. He had seen major league stadiums on television, and the recent playoff game in the factory league had been played in a minor league stadium. But this layout at West Palm Beach was far superior to that stadium. Except for the capacity of the stands, it equaled many new major league stadiums and was ahead of the older ones.

Zeke found the offices under the stands. It happened that one of the coaching staff for the Instructional League club was there. He conducted Zeke on a tour of the facility.

There were concrete stands around from third to first base with bleachers beyond the stands to the right field bullpen and along the fence to the left field bullpen. Each bullpen had two pitching mounds, two pitching slabs, and two plates at proper distance from the slabs. Benches were on the diamond side of a woven wire fence that separated bullpens from bleachers.

"The home dugout's behind third," the coach said. "Our clubhouse is on that side. Identical dugout and clubhouse for the visiting teams are on the first base side."

Zeke stood on the lip of the dugout and looked out across the diamond. A scoreboard was located in center field, a little to the right of a green background to give batters a good hitting contrast. The marker in deep center field read 410. A marker in right center and another in left center bore the numerals 395. At the foul lines, markers of 350 were fastened to the fence. There were other diamonds beyond the right and left field fences. An enclosed area behind the left field bleachers was equipped with pitching machines and canvas backdrop.

"It's big league all the way," the coach said. "Best training layout in the country, bar none." He gave Zeke a sidelong glance and added with a grin, "Don't get carried away, son. Maybe you'll make the varsity and move from here to the out-of-this-world Atlanta

Stadium; but in case you don't, any minor league setup that I know of will look like a cow pasture compared to this."

Zeke appreciated more fully the coach's comment when they moved through the door from dugout to clubhouse. Some of the placards above the well-ventilated lockers still bore the names of Atlanta Braves who had used them during spring training of the previous year.

The rookie catcher's gaze caught one lettered LUIS DANBERRO.

The first-string Braves catcher had used that now-empty locker. Zeke's awe was obvious as he stared at it. He stole surreptitious glances around as they moved on through the clubhouse. A jumble of talk came as the outside door opened; then a tanned man, Bob Naffing, broke from the entering group and came toward Zeke. He was in a uniform that had *Braves* lettered in script across the shirt front and the numeral 10 below the slanting letters. Naffing's glance slid from Zeke to the locker that Danberro had used.

"I'll say right now that you can have it," Naffing said, "just latch onto it." He extended his hand. "Welcome, Pender."

Then Naffing turned and shouted, "All right, everybody. The clubhouse boy has uniforms. Get your size from him and climb into a monkey suit and get out on the field. The Hollywood Cardinals will be here Friday to open our schedule. We can use every minute to get ready. Batting practice in fifteen minutes!"

Zeke Pender got a uniform, smoothed his hands across the *Braves* and numeral 25 on the shirt. He felt ten feet tall as he put on the cap with the letter on the bill contrasting with the dark blue color. He was out waiting at the front corner of the batting cage, watching Bob Naffing warm up a pitcher when somebody bumped him aside. Zeke turned.

"'Scuse it." The player who did the bumping spoke in a careless tone. "I always take first whacks!"

He was blond and blue-eyed, but aside from coloring he and Zeke Pender were very much alike in physical appearance. Zeke estimated that they would be no more than a fraction of an inch different in height and no more than a pound or two in weight. Their shoulder widths were about the same. Zeke said nothing, but stepped back from the corner of the batting cage.

Bob Naffing allowed a final pitch from the pitcher to slap into his mitt. "All right, Manley," Naffing said. "Take your first whacks. Lay one down and then five cuts, foul, fair, or miss."

He straightened, took off his mask and gave a level look to Roger Manley, recipient of a fat bonus from the Braves. "Suddenly it occurs to me that a better receiver than I am should be handling batting practice pitchers," Naffing said. "Take your cuts and put on your gear and take over behind the plate."

"Wha-a-at! I only get one turn!" Manley objected. "I can't—"

"—get out of it," Naffing interrupted. His brown eyes were hard as he finished Manley's sentence. "They call you Bull Manley," Naffing said in tone so low it could only be heard by someone very near. "Start bulling me and you'd better be ready to go all the way.

I said take your cuts and put on your gear. Understand?"

The burly bonus player glared at Naffing. For a moment Zeke expected a physical clash. Then Bull Manley growled something beneath his breath and stepped into the batter's box on the first base side of the plate.

One of Manley's five swings clouted the ball out of the park near the right foul marker. Two others would have been safe hits in a game. Zeke watched the bonus slugger, and the awe he felt at being in competition with Manley must have shown in his expression.

Bob Naffing stood beside Zeke after Manley took over the backstopping spot. "All right," Naffing said. "A certain amount of humility in a rookie is good, but there's a difference between humility and being overawed. Get up there at the plate with this firmly fixed in your mind: you're a natural hitter. You may be a better all around man with the bat than Manley. Relax!"

Zeke made his bunt. He thought he had the second pitch well timed. But he popped up barely ten feet in front of the plate. Bull Manley smothered the ball.

"Man, this factory league slugger really crashes that potato!" Manley called loudly, motioned toward the outfielders "Get back! Maybe the best place to play him is outside the fence!"

The taunt seemed to be what Zeke needed. He was so disgusted and determined to show Manley that he forgot to be tense.

Of his four remaining cuts, Zeke Pender slammed one over the fence in deep left center field, drilled an outside pitch on a line between the second baseman and first baseman, rapped a sharp grounder through the hole between third and short, and hit a drive on which the leftfielder made a running catch.

Naffing nodded approval when Zeke came from the batting cage and made the traditional okay sign with circled forefinger and thumb.

3 : Bull Manley, Bonus Star

THURSDAY MORNING THE Braves met for the only full day of instructive workout.

Pitchers and first basemen went with a coach to the infield beyond the right field fence. They would work on timing of plays where ground balls were hit to the right and pitcher and first baseman had to collaborate on fielding the ball and covering the bag.

Outfielders and another coach occupied the stadium field. Infielders went with a third coach to the layout beyond the left field fence. Naffing, Whitey—the clubhouse boy who had a wistful ambition to play ball—and the trio listed on the roster as catchers, went to the left field bullpen.

Zeke stole glances at Manley and Mike Oldham, the third backstop candidate, as the quintet walked to the bullpen. He liked stocky, friendly Mike. He was surprised to learn that Mike Oldham had been in the Braves' farm system several years. Each season Mike had advanced—but he had never yet been called up to the big club.

When Naffing faced the three catchers, Zeke was more awed than ever. A feeling that he was out of his depth grew stronger.

"I'm going to assume that you guys are all novice catchers," Naffing said. "Whitey, get out there on one of the pitching slabs. You and I will be the pitchers."

Bob Naffing eyed Manley, Zeke, and Mike Oldham in turn. "Very few pitches are obvious strikes, right down the middle," he said. "The catcher has a responsibility to his pitcher to receive pitches favorably to get the strike call. The umpire is the man to convince, and a catcher can never afford to forget that fact. Any movement the catcher makes to counterfeit his catch gives the umpire an excuse to call the pitch a ball. The catcher who knows how to catch pitches correctly can widen and lengthen the strike zone.

"To do so, he must stay low and give the umpire a chance to see the pitch. Whenever the catcher moves up with his body, the umpire may not have a good view as the ball comes in. You may get a ball call on a good strike. All low pitches should be caught with the mitt palm facing up and the pitch reached out for so as to catch them at strike height. Catch a low pitch 'down' or back underneath and you will most likely lose the call. Low curves should always be caught reaching out, without moving your body if possible. The umpire has a chance to see the ball at a favorable position. You might say he stops its progress in his vision for a split second at strike-zone height. Curve balls that come in high must not be reached out for if you can avoid it. The pitch will be caught unfavorably. The high curve should be caught back next to the body so the umpire gets a chance to stop it in his view at the lowest possible level as it comes in."

Naffing went on. He spoke of the importance of making a mitt-target for the pitchers; shifting ("A poor designation, in my view. More a mental preparing to catch the ball where the catcher is vulnerable.") He discussed a catcher gearing his attitude so reactions became automatic.

It was all fascinating to Zeke. He began to realize how little he knew about the fine points of catching. Then a lull came in Naffing's talk, and Roger "Bull" Manley added validity to the "cocky" assessment his mates were making of him.

"This is old stuff," Manley said. "You learn it playing Little League and high school and American Legion ball." He thumped his fist into the pocket of his mitt. "Anyway, they've always told me a guy learns best by doing!"

Zeke Pender softly drew in a breath. How could a fellow shoot off his mouth like that to a coach?

"I've been in professional baseball a long time," Naffing said after a moment. His tone was level and calm but a core of hardness underlay his words. "A pro doesn't allow personalities to influence his professional attitude. But being a pro is a two-way street. I'm leaning over backward trying to view you professionally."

Naffing's gaze traveled over Manley then returned to hold the other's eyes steadily. "It's hard to do, because I don't think you're a pro. In my book our front office went overboard in paying you any bonus. You still have to prove you're professional baseball material. One thing you'd better get set firmly in mind: in any baseball relationship we have as long as you're down here, I have to be boss. I don't intend to have you or anyone else popping off. Clear?"

Manley scowled, glared, then dropped his eyes and nodded.

"Keep repeating to yourself that this is an instructional league," Naffing added dryly. "Even a big bonus star just *might* acquire something worthwhile from professional coaching."

The burly catcher grinned. It seemed to Zeke very close to a patronizing grin. Bob Naffing paid no attention. He treated Manley the same as Mike and Zeke as he continued to elaborate on other coaching tips.

Zeke and Mike Oldham walked together from the bullpen after the catching instruction.

"Manley's a swell-headed fool!" Oldham spoke bluntly. "I hope you have more sense, Pender."

Before Zeke could make any comment, Oldham went on.

"Naffing laid things on the line when he offered me the chance to come down here. It doesn't seem to make much sense for a guy who's been kicking around six seasons in the minor leagues to be playing in an instructional league. But when you eat, drink, and breathe baseball, you aren't going to pass up anything, even when you know the best you can expect is to reach the high minors, maybe a Triple-A club. Didn't Joe McCarthy make one of the best managerial records ever without having played major league ball?

25
16
44

"So I agreed to come and give the kid catchers any help I can. I doubt that Manley would appreciate advice from me—or anybody else!" Oldham spat in disgust. "He's a double-barreled jerk, and I'll probably tell him just that before we get through!"

"Tips you can give *me* will sure be appreciated." Zeke's tone was sincere.

"It figures." Mike Oldham nodded. "I just wanted to be sure you understood before I started sounding off. You'll get plenty of coaching from Naffing—and Naffing could write the book on catching, but maybe I can add things he might miss. The chances are, though, that Manley will get first call behind the dish to start."

Manley was listed as catcher and hitting fifth in the batting order that was taped to the dugout wall for the opening game. The Cardinals went down in order in the top of the first; hitters for the Braves could do no better with the offerings of the Cardinal pitcher.

It was a pitcher's game for five and a half innings.

In the bottom of the sixth the leadoff man walked on a three-and-one pitch. The next batter was nicked by a curve that just did not break enough. In the Braves dugout, Naffing said, "When a pitcher is tiring he frequently gives the first sign by loss of control. Look 'em over, up there. This fireballer's been throwing pretty hard, he may be giving out. Work him into a hole, and you'll get a green light to hit the cripple pitch!"

The next batter was Manley. He took two pitches wide. Zeke saw the hit sign flashed from the bench to the third base coach and passed to the batter. Bull

Manley slammed a drive into the extra base lane between center and right field. It went for a triple. Two runs crossed the plate.

A solid hit through the hole between short and third scored Manley. A relief pitcher came from the Cardinal bullpen and put out the Braves' fire.

Cardinal batters did not threaten in their seventh.

Then four straight hits greeted the reliever in the bottom of the inning. A fielder's choice, a long sacrifice fly, and two walks raised the inning total to four runs and left the bases full when Manley again came to bat.

He "tied into" the second pitch. This time his drive cleared the fence in right center field. The grand slam homer made the score 11-0 for the Braves. Two more runs were added in the Braves eighth.

The Cardinals scored twice in their ninth, one on a hard-to-justify throw from Manley into the right field corner when he attempted to pick a runner off first base. But the final scoreboard figures were Braves, 13; Cardinals, 2.

"Well, you can't find much to complain about with a guy scoring two markers himself and knocking in five more," Mike Oldham said to Zeke. "Even if he did make a bonehead move that spoiled his pitcher's shutout—and that does not endear a catcher, believe me! Still you'd have to say Manley was a blamed good hitter, at least today."

The Braves won four straight, hitting and scoring as though they were going to wreck the league. Six to thirteen runs and nine to seventeen hits per game against the Yankees at Fort Lauderdale, the Pirates at West Palm Beach, and the Cardinals again at Hollywood. Manley was "a blamed good hitter" in all of them. He chalked up twelve hits against twenty-three at bats.

"Looks as though he's worth all the bonus he got." Zeke sighed outside the batting cage while Manley hit in batting practice before the fifth game. Zeke saw some of the visiting Yankees watching Manley—probably pitchers who might have to face him. "A fellow's liable never to get a chance to show what he can do," Zeke said. "Competing against anyone as hot as Manley is mighty rough."

"The pitcher scheduled to start for the Yankees today threw against Manley in a rookie league last summer," Mike said. "The word over the grapevine is he's got good stuff and plenty of moxie. The big Yankees sent their regular pitching coach down here to polish the kid. They're counting on him to go with the big club come spring. I've got a hunch a little tarnish may show through today for Golden Boy Manley."

Mike Oldham studied Manley. The big blond laid into an inside fast ball and parked it beyond the fence ten feet inside the right foul marker.

"Sometimes I think I see a weakness, and about then Manley clobbers one," Mike said. "This is a hitting ballclub and plate-power has been the trademark of the Braves for years. But the name of the game is still pitching. It could be that Manley's bonus-star shine is due to dim."

4 : Finally in a Game

THE YANKEE PITCHER lived up to "the word" that had been sent out over the grapevine. He set down batters in order in the first two Braves innings, gave up a scratch hit in the third, then kept the bases free of runners two more innings. In the sixth the Braves' leadoff batter walked, and the second man was given a scratch hit when his attempted sacrifice bunt could not be handled.

Then the Yankee pitcher really bore down. He inveigled a batter to go after a sinker outside and foul-pop to the first baseman. He got three strikes against a man for the second out.

"This is one of those can't-miss youngsters who looks as though the tag fits," Bob Naffing observed in the dugout. Naffing more often than not sat beside

Zeke Pender, and Zeke knew that his comments were not idly made. "His fast ball is live," Naffing went on. "He has a good curve that he breaks off fast and sharp, or slow and roundhouse snaky, and I've never seen a young pitcher with a better change-up."

"Must be his coach is working him to perfect his slider," Mike Oldham said from the other side of Zeke. "Improve it, anyway. He keeps trying sliders until he gets behind a hitter. Whatever he throws moves around that old plate, too."

"There's good catching out there as well as exceptional pitching." Naffing inclined his head toward the man behind the plate. "Watch the way he gives his pitcher a target. Note that he doesn't lose the tiniest fraction of an inch in receiving a pitch. Give good pitching a close look and nine times out of ten you'll find the catcher rates some of the credit—a lot of it. The right calls help mediocre or even poor pitching, and wrong calls can ruin good pitching."

The batter lofted an easy fly to end the inning, and the teams changed sides. Zeke was watching Manley. Mike Oldham was looking at the pitcher.

"Well, there's no doubt the Yankee chucker is a good one," Mike said, "but our guy's done a job out there, too. Who is he, Bob? I mean I know the public address announced him as Murphy, but I never heard of him. How come he just showed up?"

"Dennis Murphy got his high school diploma yesterday. He signed with us in mid-June, the day his class was graduated, but there was no publicity. Dennis Murphy, Sr. was determined his son would not leave off schooling until he had his high school diploma. Young Dennis had goofed off during baseball season—maybe figuring they'd graduate him anyway and if not, so what. His dad wouldn't cosign the contract until Dennis, Jr. took work in summer school and special tutoring to earn the credits he lacked. Murphy's been keeping in shape throwing for a sandlot team, so we flew him down here and put him right out there on the hill."

Naffing watched Dennis Murphy. The newcomer was a southpaw. His arms seemed exceptionally long, but that could have been due to the slenderness of his six-three height. He was well developed around the shoulders. Murphy disposed of the first batter of the inning before Naffing went on.

"Everybody in our organization who looked at him when Murphy was being scouted believes that the boy deserves the can't-miss designation. This is the first time I've seen him pitch. I'd have to say he needs to eliminate some poor pitching habits—if they aren't faults—but he has the basic stuff to make a major league pitcher."

The game went on, tight and scoreless through the seventh inning. Batters who had been terrorizing pitchers were docile this day. No runs showed on the scoreboard when the Yankee pitcher was lifted in the eighth for a pinch hitter. The strategy paid off. A two-base drive, a sacrifice bunt, and a long fly to right field scored the first run of the game.

Bull Manley had not come close to a safe hit in three times at bat. He had struck out twice. It happened that he was leadoff man in the Braves eighth. The Yankee pitcher who came in was a righthander.

His first pitch to Manley was a sweeping curve. Bull Manley swung mightily, but the pitch fooled him by not being as wide as he thought. The ball sliced off the end of the bat. He flung the club toward the dugout and started jogging halfheartedly toward first.

The third baseman had no trouble in gloving the easy roller. He had nothing but trouble *after* the ball was in his glove.

It stuck in the webbing. He clutched and pawed at it. Coaches at third and at first base yelled frantically at Manley. "Get on your horse! . . . Run, man, run! You can beat it out!"

Manley did not respond until he was about thirty feet short of first base. Then he glanced toward third and saw the infielder struggling. He put on a burst of speed. A good throw would have got him even then, but the Yankee infielder hurried too much after he finally dug the ball free. His peg was wide, in the dirt, and pulled the first baseman off the bag.

A slender player ran from the dugout and took Manley's place as base runner. The burly catcher lumbered off the diamond.

"Keep right on going into the clubhouse!" The words came in a tight tone from a coach in the dugout —not Bob Naffing. The man designated this day as manager showed white beneath the tan of his face. "We hustle on this ballclub—everybody and all the time! Don't open your trap, Manley! I'm not taking any lip from you!"

The runner was sacrificed to second by the sixth man in the batting order. The Yankee manager ordered an intentional walk to fill the empty base at first and set up a possible double play. The eighth hitter for the Braves struck out, swinging at a ball so wide and low the catcher could not handle it. Each baserunner advanced a base. Two out, tying run on third, lead run at second.

Zeke saw Naffing signal the coach who had barked at Manley. "Pender!" The coach called. "You're hitting for Murphy. A baseknock means two runs. Make him pitch to you!"

For a second's fraction Zeke Pender did not move. Then the realization that he was finally going to get into a game swept through him.

He grabbed the weighted bat near the on-deck circle, swung it with his regular bat while the umpire passed the word to the press box and the public address blared: "Your attention, please. Pender, Number 25, batting for Murphy."

Zeke felt no nervousness in the batter's box. He was always at ease with a bat in his hands. He settled his spikes, gripped the bat firmly but not too tightly, swung it across the plate several times.

The first pitch was high and tight and drove Zeke back. He merely gave the pitcher a look and settled into the same stance. Another pitch was near the strike zone but missed. Zeke did not go after it. Ball two. He looked down at the third base coach.

Manley had been given the hit sign for a two-and-nothing pitch in an earlier game, but the coach flashed the take sign. A strike whistled past Zeke. Then a fourth pitch missed. Three-and-one. Zeke looked at the coach. The bench was going all the way; the take sign flashed again.

Zeke tossed his bat away following the next pitch. He was sure it was too low, but the umpire did not agree. He called a strike. Three-and-two.

Okay, Zeke thought. *Now I don't have to look for a sign.*

Came another debatable, maybe-in-maybe-out throw. It was not his kind of pitch, but Zeke had to protect the plate. His level swing connected.

The ball was down the outside edge and in baseball parlance, Zeke "hit it where it was pitched." Not a hard drive, the ball looped over the second baseman, too high for him to catch, too shallow to be reached by the right fielder. Both runners were on the move with two out and three-and-two count.

The runs scored, there was no play at the plate, and Zeke was careful to only go a step or two after rounding first. He was not going to fall victim to a cut-off play.

Zeke was left stranded on first when the following batter fouled out, but the big rookie felt warm and good as he trotted to the dugout. A basehit his first time at bat in professional ball! Two runs batted in! They paid off on RBI's about as much as the long ball. They—

"Get your gear on, Pender." The words from the manager cut through Zeke's thoughts. "You'll catch this inning. Keep Tom working hard, now."

Zeke stumbled as he went after shin guards and protector. He had expected Mike Oldham would be put behind the plate to handle Tom Bary. The veteran was noted for explosive criticism of his catchers when things did not go smoothly.

He conferred with this man who had been pitching major league ball before Zeke Pender was born. Sent to the Florida Instructional League in hope the hot sun would bake out arm miseries, Bary was allowed to follow pretty much his own routine. He'd asked to work in the bullpen today.

"No fancy stuff, kid," Bary said. "There are enough fast balls left in the old flipper to get three of these guys out."

The first Yankee batter tied into what looked to him like a fast ball, waist high down the middle. The sphere rose noticeably an instant before the bat met it. A lazy fly drifted into center field. One out.

Another fast ball to the second hitter must have looked "fat" to him. It was not a fat pitch. His grounder to shortstop was handled routinely. Two out.

Zeke took the third pitch, mighty close to the inside of the strike zone but ruled a ball. Then the hitter topped a fast pitch that dipped instead of rising. One bounce into Bary's glove, a throw to first. Three out.

His young teammates pounded the veteran's back. He pretended to take it in stride, but Zeke saw the satisfaction in Tom Bary's eyes. Teammates slapped Zeke's back, shook his hand.

"He catches one pitch—o-n-e, count it!—and a guy'd think he'd caught a no-hitter!"

The jeering words came from a husky, blond youth in fancy sport shirt and slacks, leaning over the railing of a box in the stands next to the dugout. A sneer wrinkled Bull Manley's face.

Zeke raised his hand and grinned. Manley didn't have a chance of spoiling this wonderful moment!

5 : Kid Stuff

INSTRUCTIONAL COACHING FOR the West Palm Beach Braves was largely done during daily morning workouts. The boys were expected to be dressed and on the field by 10:30. Individual coaching in fielding, batting instruction and practice at the pitching machine cages, throwing by pitchers, work on anything a boy showed need for, and drills in defensive team play were stressed until the break at noon for a light lunch.

The club provided hot soup and rolls and beverages. The refrigerator in the room off the clubhouse always had a supply of apples and other fruit and soft drinks.

Naffing gave out mimeographed sheets from time to time. In the clubhouse following the Yankee game, he passed some around. "Note that these are headed

Organizational Cut-Offs and Relay Fundamentals," he said. "Study them. Every club in the Braves system executes these manuevers in uniform pattern. If you're moved to another club, you will find the same techniques. We've worked on them some; we're going to stress defensive play more in workouts. But we can't begin tomorrow."

He indicated a notice chalked on the blackboard fastened to the front wall of the clubhouse. BASEBALL RULES FORBID ANY PROFESSIONAL BASEBALL GAMES PLAYED DURING THE HOURS OF THE WORLD SERIES. 9:30 GAMES WILL BE PLAYED IN THE FLORIDA EAST COAST INSTRUCTIONAL LEAGUE DURING THE SERIES.

"The Series begins tomorrow," Naffing said. "Any Instructional League game not completed by twelve noon will be called and the score recorded as of the last complete inning. Be in uniform ready to go, no later than nine tomorrow morning. You're free to do what you like after the games while the Series is in progress."

Next morning Zeke was not entirely surprised at being told to warm up the starting pitcher. He expected that Manley would be catching for the game. But he also was sure that his clutch hit the day before would not go unnoticed. He thought of himself as the Number Two receiver now, and likely to be used frequently as righthanded pinch hitter.

He *was* surprised when he looked at the batting order posted on the dugout wall. "Pender, c," was listed above the pitcher. Manley was in his accustomed spot higher in the order, but behind his name today was "lb." His back to the plate while warming up the starting pitcher in the left field bullpen, Zeke had not seen that Oldham handled the plate duties during infield practice and that first base had been held down by a sulky Manley.

The Braves lost their first game that day.

Two walks, an infield hit, a long triple, and a sacrifice fly added up to a four-run first inning for the Hollywood Cardinals. Their hitters kept on working over Braves pitchers just as the Braves had mauled Cardinal pitching in their opening game.

After two hours and forty-two minutes, umpires invoked the rule that no game could be in progress during World Series play. The game was called at the end of eight innings. The score was Hollywood Cardinals, 12; West Palm Beach Braves, 4.

"It would have been nice if you could have caught a winner for your full game debut behind the plate," Naffing told Zeke in the clubhouse. "You made some mistakes, which we expected. Nothing very serious, mostly due to inexperience and things that coaching help can iron out. By and large, we're satisfied with your work. It may be just as well you ran into a clambake like this early. A catcher has to live with the fact there are games when his pitchers just don't have their stuff and have trouble getting anybody out. Then they may turn in a real pitching gem their very next turn on the mound."

Naffing headed for the showers at the far end of the clubhouse. Mike Oldham stowed his mitt on the shelf of the locker next to Zeke.

"He could have been more complimentary," Mike said. "They didn't try to run on you, and that may be because they saw you've got a buggy-whip arm. Your calls for pitches were good enough. I checked. There weren't more than a half dozen pitches I would have called differently. It could be some of them were not thrown like you'd signed, and"—Mike grinned—"it's no sure thing that pitches I'd have called for wouldn't have been clobbered. You're going to be a real fine catcher. You're already a good hitter. I'll take two-for-four at the dish and two ribbies any day!"

"Maybe you'll laugh," Zeke said, "but what in the world are ribbies?"

Mike Oldham eyed the rookie a moment, did not laugh, nodded. "It figures," Mike said. "Zeke's a name they hung on you because you're a country boy, right? Well, there're plenty of farm things us guys wouldn't know. Ribbies is baseball talk for runs-batted-in, RBI's."

Naffing stopped by Zeke as the rookie toweled after his shower. Naffing said, "Do you have any special plans for the rest of the day?"

"Why, I thought I'd watch the Series game on television."

"Good." Naffing nodded. "Every one of you kids should watch and study Series play. A friend of mine lives in Juno Beach, about ten miles north of West Palm. He's a real fan. I'm going up there to watch the game with him. How about coming along?"

"Swell!" Zeke accepted eagerly. He had wondered at times if he would ever tire of soaking up baseball knowledge from Naffing. He didn't think he would. He said, "Just say where and when to meet you."

"There isn't too much time, the game comes on at one. We'll leave from here and grab a bite to eat somewhere along the way to save time. There's a place in Juno Beach that specializes in seafood and steaks. We'll all go there for dinner afterward."

Zeke Pender had never seen an ocean, except a glimpse of the Atlantic from a balcony at the Town House Motel where the Braves were quartered. Naffing's friend lived less than two hundred yards from the beach. Two large windows in the living room provided a wide view of the ocean and beach. The stocky, gray-haired gentleman and his motherly wife made Zeke feel at home, as though he had known them a long time.

The ocean fascinated Zeke. He watched an oil tanker going south. "It's a mile or mile and a quarter out," their host said, "inside the Gulf Stream. It doesn't seem more than a hundred yards when the air's clear like today."

"Gosh," Zeke said. "You sit right here in an easy chair and watch ships go by. That's something! It's the first for-real ship I've ever seen."

The game began. Shots of the catchers giving signs to the pitchers were shown several times. The elderly gentleman said, "There's a thing I've wondered about, Bob. I've read about sign stealing. Couldn't the opposing team set up a television set—say in the passageway from dugout to clubhouse—and read the signs?"

"Sure, if they could get away with it, which they couldn't. The Commissioner's office checks things pretty closely. Even if they read the signs, though, there wouldn't be enough time for the batter to get the information. More likely than not they'd end up by getting a hitter skulled when the pitcher busted a high fast one up there with the batter stepping into what was signaled as a breaking pitch."

Then Naffing said to Zeke, "Watch those catchers. They drop their glove below the left knee and any sign-stealing view of the third base coach is effectively shut out. See how they lay the signaling fingers well back along the thigh to make it tougher for a nosy batter to glimpse. Watch how they flash a flock of signs. One signal tells the pitcher which sign is the call for the pitch the catcher wants. These are frequently changed. Special care is taken when a baserunner gets on second."

Zeke nodded. His lips moved. Naffing said curiously, "What are you doing?"

"I remember better if I actually say things over to myself. When I get to my room, I write them down. I'm getting quite a book on catching."

"Good stuff." Naffing nodded approval. "Keep a book on hitters and the best pitches of each man you catch and you'll be a lot more valuable to your chuckers and the ballclub."

This was a fast-moving game. In the eighth inning a pitcher got into trouble. His manager came out from the bench, the catcher stalked to the mound. Naffing's friend said, "How about a situation like this, Bob? Does the manager ask the catcher whether the pitcher is losing his stuff? What dialogue is there?"

"There is no set procedure. Contrary to popular belief, managers seldom put the pitcher and catcher on the spot by asking bluntly. They know that pitchers are a sensitive lot. But if signs of shakiness have been apparent and the manager is thinking of making a change, he wants to know. He and his catcher may have prearranged signals, like some key word, innocent-sounding to the pitcher, or a phrase such as 'the ball isn't sinking' or 'those guys just happened to catch a curve that hung.'

"When I was managing, I had a sign with a catcher that a closed fist meant our chucker did not have good stuff. Of course, the manager may be out there just to give his man a moment to settle. He may simply tell the pitcher to mix in more off-speed pitches or inform both battery men they're being too fine and careful and getting behind the hitters as a result."

The gray-haired man nodded, then looked at the screen. The relief pitcher brought from the bullpen was just starting his range-finding tosses.

"As long as you're talking, Bob," the elderly man said, "I've been wondering about something while you've been giving pointers to the boy, here. Sometime back you told me that you're on special assignment. Just what does a man on special assignment do?"

"Oh, I scout players of other organizations, majors and minors, so we have a line on players we might be interested in trading for. I go to help any of our scouts in signing a prospect. I might be sent to any of our clubs as a trouble-shooter in special instances."

"Is Zeke a special instance? Are you trouble shooting down here?"

"No trouble." Naffing frowned. "No trouble with Zeke, at least. You might say he's a special instance." Naffing looked toward Zeke. "I guess you're solid enough to stand hearing me let down my hair a little," Naffing said. Then he looked out the window as though gathering his thoughts.

"It happens that our Farm Director, our General Manager, and a couple of scouts and myself are in some disagreement over the Braves' future catching picture. I've contended that we had little, if any, major league catching potential coming up. The club has considerable money invested in Manley and one or two others. I'm convinced that none of them can do the job.

"I am also convinced that Zeke Pender has the potential. I'm down here to develop and help bring out that potential."

Naffing looked at the television screen. A commercial cartoon had taken over.

"It's no secret that I'm not sold on Manley," Naffing continued. "He has weakness at bat and more behind the plate. I may be sticking my neck out, maybe could lose my job if I'm 'way wrong, but—well, I'm not going to mention Manley's weaknesses. We're trying to work with him to eliminate them. But he's a difficult kid to help—in my book, impossible to coach if he doesn't change his attitude."

Naffing looked at Zeke. "Have you spotted any Manley weaknesses at bat?" Naffing asked.

"He hasn't looked to me as though he had any."

"Which only shows you aren't studying our hitters." Naffing shook his head. "Some of them may be with other clubs someday. You may be calling for pitches you hope they can't hit. A man making baseball his profession never stops studying and learning any more than a successful fellow in any other profession does. Teammates, opponents, any player that comes under his observation should be studied and catalogued."

The game was resumed. One of the catchers thought the plate umpire missed a call. He put up an argument. The argument became a full-fledged rhubarb, and his manager rushed from the dugout and pushed the irate catcher away.

"Letting an unpire know you think he missed a call is okay," Naffing said. "Umps are human, they make mistakes. But a catcher should keep in mind that they *are* human. Go too far and you're not going to come out ahead—and you may get tossed out of the game. You have to keep in mind that the umpire calls balls and strikes. Professional umpires are competent —or they don't last—but never forget they're subject to the same tensions and resentments and impulses as the rest of us."

Zeke Pender thought about the things Naffing had said, after he was back in his room at Town House. He treasured Naffing's interest in himself. He knew that the man was dedicated to doing the best job he could to advance the skills of players in the Atlanta Braves organization. He also felt that Naffing could be as tough as was necessary in handling fellows who showed they needed rough treatment.

Zeke's feeling was borne out the next morning when the players assembled for the bus trip to Hollywood to meet the Cardinals.

Dennis Murphy looked miserable. His face was a shiny red, and his eyes were swollen. He winced as he turned, and his sport shirt rubbed against his shoulders. He said, "Zowie! Am I ever sunburned!"

Bob Naffing addressed Manley, standing next to the young southpaw pitcher. "You and Murphy left the clubhouse together yesterday, Manley," Naffing said. "What happened?"

"Nothing happened."

"Where'd you go?"

"We drove up to Riviera Beach."

"And?"

"Is it a crime to do a little water skiing? You told us we had time to ourselves after the game. So we stayed out a little too long and got sunburned. A guy gets fooled by this Florida sun."

Manley looked around the group. To Zeke the burly blond seemed very smug. Manley said, "I might be able to catch today, but it's for sure my sunburn wouldn't let me play first. All that bending and reaching and running and stuff!"

"And stuff!" Naffing spat. "Who do you think you're putting on? How is there suddenly more bending and reaching and running to playing first base than in catching? But check with the trainer. And also figure that every day you miss will be deducted from your pay!"

Naffing walked abruptly away. Manley growled beneath his breath; then when Naffing was out of hearing, muttered aloud, "How do you like that? Put a guy on the griddle just because he didn't realize how this Florida sun can bite!"

Mike Oldham moved to stand in front of Manley. "I happen to know that you spent six weeks in the rookie league at Sarasota after you were signed," Mike said. "The same Florida sun shines over Sarasota. You knew how 'this Florida sun can bite.' What you figured to gain by taking Murphy with you and getting him burned is beyond me, but I'm sure of this: pulling kid stuff like that makes you top man in the league of double-barreled jerks!"

6 : Strong Finish—Too Late

ZEKE PENDER CAUGHT the game at Hollywood. Bull Manley played first base. The Braves lost 5-4 and the run that beat them was unearned all the way.

Manley fielded a twisting grounder off the bat of the leadoff man in the Cardinal eighth. He threw the ball to the pitcher hustling over to cover first base. The throw was far too hard and behind the pitcher. The sphere rolled to the stands before Zeke, backing up the play, could retrieve it, and the runner kept right on going to second.

Another grounder was hit to Manley. He bobbled it and lost any chance to make a play at third. A fly to center field by the next hitter scored the winning run from third base.

"We might better have had somebody who knows

how to play first," Mike Oldham growled, "even if the trainer wouldn't go along with Manley's beef that he was too burned. I know this is Instructional League ball and the main idea is to try out guys, but a ball-game's a ballgame. I hate to lose. That Manley character'll never make a first baseman, anyway!"

Zeke was behind the plate against the Yankees next day. Tom Bary asked to start on the mound, to go as far as he could. The veteran set down the Yankees with only one safe hit in four innings. The Braves scored twice in their third when Zeke's two-base hit drove in one run and he scored the other himself.

He felt great as he took Bary's final warmup toss in the fifth inning and pegged to second base.

Tom Bary got the leadoff batter into a one-two count. Zeke consulted the mental book he had on this hitter. He signed for a change-up, inside. Bary wriggled his glove to signify he wanted a sign for a different pitch.

Zeke signed for a curve, inside. Again the veteran pitcher shook him off. *Good fast ball hitter. Sometimes goes for inside curve or slider or change-up. Guards the plate well.* Zeke repeated in his mind what he had set down in his book on the batter. Reluctantly the rookie catcher signed for a fast ball.

It was slammed fairly and hard. A foot more height and the ball would have cleared the fence to the right of the 395 marker in left center field. It hit the fence and rebounded into a fielder's hand, but the batter slid into third ahead of the relay throw.

Now Bary brought out the craftiness that years of clutch pitching had developed. He worked the second batter into a three-and-two count. Zeke signed for a curve, half expecting to be shaken off. He wasn't. Bary threw a good curve and the batter was caught so badly off balance that he did not even offer at the pitch. One out.

Bary earned the second out by coaxing a batter to go for a change-up and pop to shortstop. He worked carefully on the fourth Yankee to come to the plate. Shaking off Zeke's sign twice, Bary tried to slip a half-speed pitch past the hitter. The Yankee all but leaped at what was to him a fat pitch. His swing was the out-of-the-park type, but it was mistimed. He undercut the ball. A foul bored into the sky between home and the Yankee dugout.

Zeke Pender turned the right way, jerked off his mask and flung it well away as he located the ball. He was under it, waiting. Then a freak gust of wind caught the high popup. The ball swept back toward the

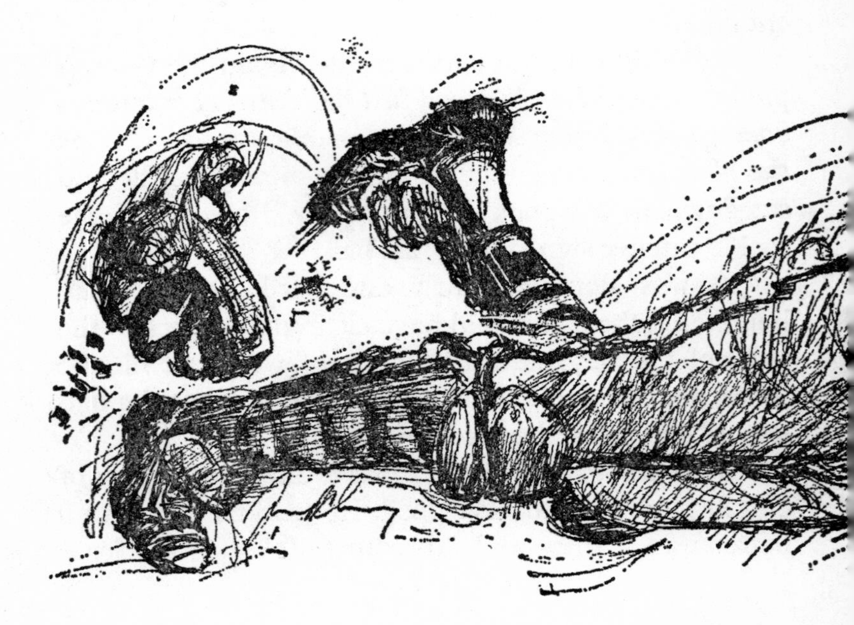

plate as though a giant hand had batted it out of course.

The rookie reversed himself, ran four steps and saw that he was barely going to reach the ball. He extended his mitt as far as possible, strained hard, stepped into his discarded mask and fell flat on his face. The ball hit the side of his mitt and rolled along the ground.

Zeke carried the ball almost to the mound after he'd scrambled to his feet. "Gosh," he said, "I'm awfully sorry. You should be out of the inning. Pitch over my error, will you?"

Tom Bary did not "pitch over" it, and Zeke's misfortune went into the records as an error when the batter whaled the next pitch into the extra base lane between center and right fielders. The veteran pitcher shook off Zeke's signs three times on the next two bat-

ters. Each of them hit the ball solidly. Two more Yankee runs counted before they were retired.

Those three runs beat the Braves, 3-2.

The drain in the shower-room floor was nowhere near as low as Zeke Pender after the game. *Too slow and awkward . . . pitchers wouldn't have confidence in you.* Words the manager of his factory league team had said echoed in the rookie's thoughts. He glanced across the quiet dressing quarters where Tom Bary sat staring. Zeke approached the veteran pitcher. The least he could do was let Bary know how badly he felt. Tom Bary looked up.

"Stow it, kid!" Bary didn't wait for Zeke to speak. "I can't stand alibis or excuses! A man can't write off having a game lost for him, just because somebody's sorry!"

Mike Oldham waited until they were dressed before he said anything to Zeke.

"Some of the blame for that mask thing is mine," Mike said. "I should have told you over and over and long before now that every catcher should hang onto the mask until he's ready to grab a high pop. When the ball's so close to being down you're sure you won't have to run over it, heave the mask and you're safe."

Mike Oldham scowled. "It's for sure you didn't lose Bary's ballgame," he went on. "You made three mistakes and not carrying your mask with you was one. The second mistake was in letting Bary get away with shaking you around the way he did. Okay, so he's an old head and knows how to pitch. Any chucker is apt to overrate his pitches and the one he thinks is the best may be the poorest. The catcher usually knows more about his pitcher's stuff than the guy himself. The third and least excusable goof you made was in going to him in the clubhouse. Right after he's lost a tough ballgame is no time to try to soothe any pitcher!"

Zeke said, "All that doesn't change the fact that I booted an inning-ending out!"

"True, too true. It also doesn't change the fact that Bary shook you off and threw the leadoff man the wrong pitch." Mike Oldham whacked Zeke's shoulder. "You've got to learn not to wear your chin at shin-guard level, man! A guy named Pender has got to believe in himself. You're a *catcher,* Zeke. Hang on to *that* fact!"

The Braves had been on top of the four-team Instructional League since the schedule opened. But the day after losing to the Yankees, those same pests from Fort Lauderdale tied the Braves for the lead. The Pirates dropped the Braves at Municipal Stadium, 7-3, and the Yankees outlasted the Cardinals in a 12-11 slugfest.

Bull Manley sounded off in the clubhouse. "A club that keeps shifting guys around out of their regular spots won't ever go very far. They always told me a winning club has to have good pitching and good catching. We don't have much of either these days!"

The Braves traveled to Hallandale and lost the league-lead-tie. Pirate hitters sprayed offerings of Braves pitchers to all parts of the field. They counted eleven runs; the Braves attack came up with a meager three hits and one run.

Zeke Pender did not feel at all elated that two of the three hits—and the RBI—came from his bat.

Bull Manley caught the Cardinal game at Hollywood the next day. The Cardinals pounded four pitchers to the tune of seventeen hits and nine runs. Manley's bases-empty homer in the fifth saved the Braves from being shut out.

Midway of the fifty-four game schedule, the Braves had dropped to second place, three games behind the leading Yankees. In the next ten days they dropped to last place in the standings. The first Sunday in November they won the second game of a double-header. From there they lost until they had a seventeen won and twenty-two lost record the fifteenth of the month.

Bob Naffing and the other coaches held a meeting before the workout Monday morning.

"We're not the first club to go into a slump," Naffing said. "We won't be the last. But losing so many ballgames in any league is not good. We've got to pull out of the slump. The best way is for every man to grit his teeth and put out more team effort. We aren't hitting; our fielding is sloppy; our pitching ranges from awful to horrible.

"Batting practice may improve our hitting. This morning we'll split into groups to utilize all the facilities we have for batting. Bat and bat and bat. Three diamonds and the pitching machine cages. Coaches will tell you where to go to and pitch to you. Get out there now, everybody but pitchers and catchers."

Naffing waited until the clubhouse held only the twelve pitchers, himself, and the three catchers on the roster. When he spoke there was no softness in Naffing's tone.

"We've been on the short end because of lousy pitching in as many games as we've lost for lack of runs." Naffing let his gaze rest on Tom Bary. "This goes for every one of you pitchers," Naffing said. "Bickering and shaking your catcher around is bush league, in my book. In any case, it's out. That doesn't mean you can't shake off *any* sign. It does mean that we're putting the responsibility for calling pitches squarely where it belongs—on the catchers."

Naffing eyed Manley and Zeke. He seemed to include Mike Oldham as a kind of afterthought.

"Beginning with the Atlanta Braves at the top, right down through all our clubs to rookie leagues, we want our catchers to be jockeys who'll ride guys into line and keep them there. Our catchers are our quarterbacks. They're in direct control on the field. We make no bones about declaring that when a club gets down, the finger of blame can be pointed toward the catcher. I'm pointing that finger at you catchers right now.

"Starting today, whichever of you is back of the plate, you keep the ballclub alert and on its toes. You call the pitches. If any pitcher shakes you off, go out to the mound after the third time and tell him he's through. The bench will back you up!"

Naffing again looked briefly at each of the trio of catchers. He said suddenly, "Oldham will work today's game. I'm counting on you to show Manley and Pender how a real catcher handles his pitcher, Mike!"

That was the day the Braves gave evidence of coming out of their slump. They finally lost a ten-inning 4-3 decision. Mike Oldham shook his head in the clubhouse.

"I'd like to catch every game," Mike told Zeke, "but I'm beginning to see things the way Naffing has been trying to get me to see them. The team may lose as much with my weak bat as they gain from a good job of defensive catching—and I say without egotism that I *am* a good defensive catcher. Thing is—well, Bob had better have you in there—or even Manley."

"You were robbed of an extra base hit in the seventh. That rightfielder was out of position or he would never have reached the ball."

"Wrong, Zeke. The Yankee catcher's a smart cookie. He signaled his outfield where to play because he was going to have his pitcher feed me fast balls, and he knows I don't get the bat around quickly enough to pull fireballs. He worked me perfectly in the tenth when all I had to do was get the ball out of the infield to drive in the tying run. Nope, Naffing knows all this. It'll be you or Manley from here on in—probably more you."

Mike's prophecy proved out.

Zeke Pender caught the next day. Score: Braves, 6; Cardinals, 5.

Manley caught a game at Fort Lauderdale. Score: Braves, 7; Yankees, 2.

Tom Bary went all the way against the Pirates in Municipal Stadium and did not shake off a single pitch that Zeke signed for. Score: Braves, 5; Pirates, 1.

They lost to the Cardinals at Hollywood.

Zeke Pender hit his first grand slam home run in professional ball and pulled the Braves to a 6-5 lead in the ninth. But in the bottom of the inning a walk, a sacrifice, a bloop single over first, tied the score. The runner on first was off for second on the first pitch to the fourth batter. Zeke had anticipated a steal attempt, called for a pitchout, and his bullet-peg was on target while the runner was three strides away from the bag. The difficulty was that shortstop and second baseman had got crossed up on their sign as to who would cover. Neither was there to take Zeke's perfect peg.

Under full speed, the runner raced to third and was waved on home by the coach. Zeke had to reach to his right for the throw from center field. He whirled and dove to put the tag on the runner but the Yankee was already sliding across the plate.

That was the final loss of the season for the Braves.

They closed out the schedule with ten straight victories. Zeke Pender caught seven of the winning streak. The club statistician turned over to the Farm Director's office a fine .348 batting average for Zeke. He had hit five homers, two triples, and four doubles with singles enough to bring his RBI total to twenty-eight.

Yet, when Mike Oldham expressed his feeling in the clubhouse after the final game, Zeke was in whole-hearted agreement.

"Ten straight is okay for any club any time, and there's no doubt we're the best ballclub down here," Mike said. "But we finished second, and that ruins the whole thing. A strong finish but too late is better than nothing, but—well, I'll see you guys at Waycross."

PART TWO

Farm Club's Training Camp to Florida State League

7 : Farm Club's Camp

"HOLD IT, no need to come across!"

Zeke looked around at the words. Mike Oldham was headed toward the car Zeke had parked near the bus station. Mike continued, "Welcome to Waycross, Georgia, spring home of Atlanta Braves farm clubs." He stuck out his hand toward Zeke. "Man, you look the same as you did a dozen weeks back at West Palm Beach! How the heck did you keep your tan through the winter? Sun lamp?"

"No lamp, just sun." Zeke grinned. "Mom and I spent time driving around every day after I bought this used convertible. We got a reputation for being off our rockers, driving with the top down. Mom's always loved being outdoors in any kind of weather."

Zeke looked Mike over, nodded, and said, "You

look fit and ready to go." Then he asked, "How come you wrote me to come a day early? And why didn't you send directions how to get to the camp site after I wrote I'd be here but would be driving?"

"There wasn't time. I figured you'd come to the bus station anyway. I was planning on us rooming together, but when I contacted Bob Naffing about assigning us to the same tepee, I found out some changes have been made." Mike abruptly seemed embarrassed. "I'll drive," he said. "It's a kind of tricky six miles to camp until you know the route."

"Mike, about these changes: have you had word from the Braves brass to report for spring training with the big club at West Palm Beach? Or maybe with the Triple A club?" Zeke asked.

"Thanks for the compliment." Mike smiled. "I wish you were right." He started the car and edged it into the traffic stream. He drove for several blocks without saying more. Then as they moved away from downtown Waycross, Mike said, "It's maybe not such a big deal, Zeke, but it's a thing I've been building toward. Naffing stopped by my home last week and laid things right on the barrel head.

"I could come here as a candidate for catcher and probably be assigned to a Double A farm club, perhaps even Triple A, although that was a big perhaps. Or I could come here with a contract as a coach. That might lead to a manager's job, so that's what I chose."

"Aren't you too young to give up active playing, Mike?"

"Well, depending on how things work out, I might end up being on some roster as player-coach," Mike said. "About the young part—I'll be thirty this year. I didn't get into pro ball till I was nearly twenty-four. Thirty is middle age for a ballplayer, Zeke, especially a guy who hasn't yet made it to the big time."

Zeke said nothing. After a while Mike Oldham went on talking.

"A guy can always dream," he said. "I'll probably never be another Joe McCarthy, but I can keep in mind that McCarthy won a pennant managing the Chicago Cubs and steered the Yankees to pennants and world championships. And Joe McCarthy never played major league ball!"

Mike went on, mentioning names of famous managers who had been catchers in their playing days, as though strengthening his chances: Connie Mack of the famous Philadelphia Athletics, when they ruled the American League; Mickey Cochrane, a catcher for the Athletics, who went on to manage Detroit to two pennants and a World Series championship; Del Baker, a former catcher who succeeded Cochrane.

"In later years," he summed up, "Al Lopez won pennants at Ceveland and for the Chicago White Sox and is accepted as one of the all-time great managers. Ralph Houk caught some for the Yankees before he managed them to pennants. Yogi Berra won a pennant the first year he managed the Yankees. Birdie Tebbetts managed the Braves and afterward the Cleveland Indians."

Mike swerved the convertible off a main blacktop road and drew up beside a long white barracks-type building. Lettered near the front corner was the word T-E-P-E-E and a numeral inside a diamond.

"We call them tepees but they were built as barracks for Air Force training lads years ago," Mike said. "They make good quarters for players and coaches while farm club personnel gets in shape every spring. Tepees One, Two, Three, and Four face the road, and that one in front across the road is the recreation hall.

"The cafeteria is the one farthest back, and Tepee Number Five is off to one side. You're assigned to Tepee Number Two. I'll be in the tepee where all coaches and managers are quartered. You can select a room and have a roommate assigned later, or you can take a bed in the big room at the back called the squad room."

"I'll take the squad room," Zeke said.

"Okay. Stow your stuff, and get a uniform from Supply. We may as well get in a little preliminary work."

Zeke lost no time in donning uniform and spikes. He did not bother with shin guards or protector or mask. He and Mike would use only catcher's mitts and a ball today.

The playing area was across the road from the barracks. Mike said, "There are five diamonds, but only four are normally used." He indicated a layout near the road. "That's Number One diamond. Number Two is back of it. Three and Four are on the other side of the rotunda."

"The rotunda?"

Mike inclined his head toward a building in the middle of the four-diamond area. It reminded Zeke of the roofed but open-sided bandstand in the park back home.

"Bob Naffing stands up here and directs workouts," Mike said. "He keeps things humming and the same maneuvers going on all the diamonds. You'll find out."

Mike stopped at one of three pitching and catching setups. Nearby were three pitching machines, placed inside areas enclosed to form elongated batting cages.

"Maybe I should wait and let you get the word from Naffing," Mike said, "in case you might have objections. There's a special angle to the coaching job Naffing outlined for me. He wants me to be most concerned with a guy named Zeke Pender."

"Fine with me," Zeke said. "You can teach me plenty. Is Manley going to be in on the special instruction?"

"Manley won't be here. Naffing wasn't very communicative, but I gathered he was not exactly pleased with the decision from top brass. Manley reports at West Palm Beach for spring training with the major league club."

Mike Oldham worked with Zeke on proper shifting.

"I agree with Naffing that the word *shift* should be eliminated in teaching catching," Mike said. "Somewhere along the line a coach drilled into me that what you really have to do is be prepared to catch a ball where your glove isn't. You have to anticipate and prepare yourself mentally to catch the kind of pitch you've signed for—but—wherever it goes. Then what 'shifting' is necessary will come automatically as a reflex action."

After a while Mike noticed that Zeke had a tendency to make a fist of his right hand. Mike shook his head.

"Somebody gave you the same wrong advice that I was given," he said. "It's a fallacy to believe that tucking the thumb in the palm and closing the fingers over it will make you immune to finger damage.

"Look, Zeke." Mike illustrated. "The hand should be open at the catch in order to slap it over the ball. There's no way it can be opened quickly from a closed or clenched position without tensing the fingers in extension. Tensed fingers are more susceptible to injury.

"Keep your hand relaxed at the catch, in the position you'd hold it if you were receiving change after paying somebody in a small-town store."

They worked on other techniques. Finally Mike said, "We'd better call it quits. The cafeteria won't be in operation until tomorrow. We'll have to drive somewhere to eat."

Walking to the tepee area, Zeke said, "Sometimes it seems to me that everybody is hipped on catching. I'm not complaining, understand. I know I've got plenty to learn. What I mean is—is—well, you know what I mean."

"I guess so." Mike nodded. "I had it drilled into me long ago how important catching is to a ballclub. Did you ever hear of Gabe Paul?"

"General manager of some big league club?"

Mike nodded. "Cleveland, I guess, when he was quoted. Anyway, he said that a good team starts with good catching. Paul Richards, another former catcher I forgot to include in my list of managers, brought Clint Courtney—a blamed good catcher himself when he was in his prime—to Houston to coach their young catchers.

"Atlanta Braves brass are hep baseball men. They recognize the importance of good catching as well as Gabe Paul or Paul Richards. Right now, Luis Danberro gives them as good first-line catching as any club in the league. But Danberro is getting no younger, and there just isn't much talent backing him up."

Mike Oldham smiled wryly.

"The hope that I might make it to the big club as a backup for Danberro has been in the back of my mind for years. But there was always my bunt-size bat! You carry a man-size warclub, Zeke. You're a natural hitter. For my money, you can be in Danberro's class as a receiver. It's pretty much up to you."

8 : Grow Up!

ZEKE PENDER MADE a vow to himself the morning the Atlanta Braves farm clubs began spring training. *If it's up to me, as Mike said, I'm going to make it all the way to backup man for Danberro!*

Naffing and Oldham and every coach and manager at the Waycross camp would do everything they could to develop any player. They would do all they could to help a big, awkward, slow country boy named Pender.

"You've never been to a camp Bob Naffing runs," Mike Oldham told the rookie. "If you think we worked a tight thing in the Instructional League, wait'll you sample the program Naffing sets up here. They—guess I should say 'we' now—really pour it on."

The fact that Mike knew what he was talking

about became very clear. From the batting practice that went on endlessly at the cages surrounding the pitching machines or on one of the four diamonds to the final ball tossed in the day's workout, everybody had something to do. It seemed that there were as many coaches as players, the way they all had eyes in the backs and sides of their heads. Shouts filled the air constantly.

"All right, shortstop, you have to back up the throw to second! . . . On your horse out there! . . . Keep moving; hustle! . . . You made the throw to the wrong base. Always know what you're going to do with the ball if it comes to you! . . . Level swing, level swing! Keep that club level with the ground if you have to stoop to do it!"

It rained the second day, and practice was cut short. Coaches conducted groups of players through the back room of the recreation hall. On the walls were large charts with spaces for players' names and columns lettered Red, Blue, Orange, Green, Silver Sluggers, Injured players, Released, Did not report. Space was provided for such information as hits, walks, times on base, errors; and for pitchers, innings worked, hits against them, bases on balls, speed, curve, change-up, poise.

"Every player is evaluated every day," Mike Oldham said to the group Zeke was in. "Red, Blue, etc. are merely designations. You may play for Orange one day and with Silver Sluggers the next. There is no significance as to who is being considered for Austin or Yakima or West Palm Beach or any other club."

Bob Naffing delivered a short talk to the players.

"This will be the only time that what I'm going to say is said: you are professionals. To get anywhere in your chosen work you must keep in mind all the time that success in anything requires application and desire. You can't be carefree kids any more.

"Practice can become downright drudgery. But competition, the realization that you're graded on attitude and development of skills and techniques, knowing that you'll go up or down chiefly on what you show here at Waycross, should provide incentive to ride over hard work, even drudgery. Every one of you has our earnest wish for good luck, but don't think you can depend on luck alone to get you by."

"Boy, he sure sounds hardboiled tough." Dennis Murphy happened to be in Zeke's group. Mike Oldham heard the southpaw.

"Step out of line and you'll find out he doesn't just *sound* tough," Mike said. "This isn't American Legion or sandlot or high school ball, kid, this is for real. Take it from a guy who learned the hard way—it's dog-eat-dog in professional ball!"

"Let 'im dish it out!" Murphy's tone was defiant. "I can take it!"

"A guy has to play things the way he sees them," Mike said. "It could be you picked up some wrong ideas from Bull Manley last fall."

Zeke looked at the lefthander. He had a strong feeling that Dennis Murphy was more whistling-past-the-cemetery than anything.

Before the end of the first week, Naffing had four games going every afternoon. He stood in the rotunda, and any player who loafed or goofed on a play was liable to wonder how Naffing could be aware of everything that went on.

Dennis Murphy was pitching to Zeke one afternoon. The leadoff batter in the fourth inning topped an outside fast ball and dribbled a roller to the right of the mound not far from the foul line. The first baseman had only to move two steps to his right. It was a routine grounder that a first baseman would take all the way himself.

Zeke automatically moved down the line behind the batter, just in case the pitcher covered the bag and the toss from the first baseman was bad. On every such play, a mental picture flashed in Zeke's brain. He would never forget the wild throw Bull Manley had made in an Instructional League game.

He was not aware that Murphy had already drawn a sharp reminder from a coach earlier that day that a pitcher had fielding responsibilities. It did not occur to Zeke that Murphy would be loafing, making only a token gesture toward covering first base. The first baseman would handle the easy grounder and make the putout.

Then the picture changed abruptly. The ball hit a rough spot, a clump of hard clay, something. It eluded the first baseman's grab. He leaped after it, but by the time he got hold of the sphere, he was too far away to beat the runner to the bag—and Dennis Murphy was too far from the base to reach the first baseman's toss. The ball sailed untouched across the base.

Zeke fielded it, drew back his arm, and the runner quickly gave up any idea of trying for second. Then Dennis Murphy compounded his fielding lapse. He pulled the bill of his cap until it was over one ear, made a goofy face while he held his gloved hand at arm's length for Zeke's toss. Zeke wondered afterward how much Murphy's clowning contributed to the cutting observation that came from Bob Naffing.

"This is *not* a tryout for television comedians, Murphy! There's nothing funny about a guy dogging it, especially after he's been reminded once! If you have a lingering idea that because the club paid out good dough to get you to sign you're above coaching, forget it! Leave the ball on the mound, we'll bring a pitcher in who came to play! Twenty-five wind sprints for you and get your shower!"

"Okay!" Murphy glared defiantly. "If that's the way you want it! They always told me a pitcher was supposed to pitch and—"

"Knock it off!" The fierce whisper from Mike Oldham cut through Murphy's words: "Leave the ball and get going. Lousy kid stuff! Grow up!"

Dennis Murphy did not crumble visibly. He shrugged, more swaggered than trotted, deep beyond the foul line in right field to start the wind sprints.

"Naffing really chewed the kid out later," Oldham told Zeke after the evening meal. "I don't know. Murphy could have picked up a lot of wrong slants from Manley, but you can share the responsibility."

"Me? Gosh, I was backing up the play!"

"But you didn't see that Murphy was loafing. At least you didn't yell at him." Mike Oldham shook his head. "I told you once that you had to get confidence in Zeke Pender. Part of having confidence is not hanging back when some guy needs yelling at. You're not in the ballgame on a rain check or something!"

Mike drew in a breath. "There are things about being a coach that're rougher than playing," he said. "It's a blamed shame to see a kid with Murphy's potential rearing down the wrong road. I just don't know whether Naffing got to him."

That night, after Tepee Number Two had quieted, Zeke learned that Naffing had "got to" Dennis Murphy. Usually Zeke was asleep seconds after his head hit the pillow. This night he was thinking of things Mike had said, mostly about Zeke Pender sharing the responsibility for Murphy's goof. At first he was not sure of the noise he heard. He strained his ears. There was no doubt.

The sound came again, a muffled sob from Dennis Murphy.

Zeke proposed the next morning that he and Murphy take a room together. He never mentioned knowing how really low Dennis Murphy had been that night after putting up the defiant front to Naffing. Through their talks during the next two weeks, Zeke and Dennis Murphy drew closer and closer.

"You're good for the kid," Mike Oldham remarked. "Murphy's taking coaching the way an eager rookie should. He's settled down."

"We're good for each other," Zeke said. "It's funny, Mike. I never had a brother, but Denny's like one. He's going to be eighteen next week, and I'll be nineteen in May; but I feel like an older brother toward him, say ten years older instead of ten months."

"Yeah." Mike nodded. "You are, as far as maturity of judgment, and like that. He's always been a Dennis-the-Menace type, carefree, shoving his feet under his old man's table every day for three squares and no sweat. You've been out bucking the facts of life. Some of you is bound to rub off on Murphy. And it won't do you any harm to kind of wet-nurse him. Maybe it'll develop your confidence and responsibility."

Zeke thought of Mike's "wet-nursing" term one day the following week. He was tired after the workouts and catching a seven-inning practice game. He had no desire to drive into town.

"You've *got* to drive me in!" Dennis Murphy protested when Zeke shook his head at his request. "It's my birthday, extra special, besides. Please, Zeke?"

Zeke finally gave in. He and Dennis drove into Waycross. It was a beautiful spring night. *Warm and smelling like things will in a couple of months up home,* Zeke thought. Murphy directed him. They pulled into the parking space near an automobile agency. Zeke noted idly that the agency handled the same make of car as his convertible. Then he noted not so idly the convertible parked outside the salesroom entrance.

"Not much different-looking from yours," Murphy said. "I guess that's why I wanted it. She's mine, Zeke! Ain't she beautiful?"

"Ready to go, Mr. Murphy." The words came from a smiling man who came from the salesroom. "Title registration and insurance taken care of, tank full of gas, everything as you directed over the phone."

Zeke stood looking at the shiny new convertible. He shot a glance at Dennis Murphy. The slender youth grinned.

"This is the extra special part," Murphy said. "Part of the deal when I signed with the Braves was a new car. Dad held out that I wasn't to have my own car until I was eighteen. Well, I'm eighteen today. Get in, Zeke, we'll try her out!"

No qualms, no premonitions bothered Zeke as he settled into the seat beside Dennis Murphy. It would be relaxing to enjoy a drive without the responsibility of driving. They headed out on Route U.S. 82.

They did not drive far on Route 82 before there ceased to be anything relaxing about the drive. Dennis Murphy stepped on the gas feed; the convertible roared along the wide highway. Zeke squirmed, said, "You shouldn't drive a new car so fast, Denny."

"They make cars these days set to ring the bell right off!"

A marker lettered BLACKSHEAR came toward them fast. Dennis Murphy was glancing at the rear-view mirror. Zeke turned and saw the flashing light atop a car some distance behind.

Murphy ducked off Route 82 in Blackshear, wheeled the convertible onto Georgia 121. They followed 121 to Hoboken. Murphy fed the car gas, and the powerful new engine responded. The flashing light receded further behind.

"It's a police car, and he's definitely following us," Zeke said. "He'll catch us eventually, and it'll be worse than if you slowed and let him take us now."

"Huh-uh." Murphy shook his head. "I'll lose him. I'd *better* lose him! I haven't got a driver's license yet!"

They took U.S. 84 out of Hoboken and sped toward Waycross. The lights of the police car did not again show in the mirror. Murphy said, "I knew I could lose him!"

"Big stuff!" Zeke made no attempt to hide his disgust. "So he got stuck at cross traffic or a train crossing held him up, so what? If he was ever close enough to get your license number, you're cooked. It was a fool stunt all the way!"

Zeke got out at a corner. Before he started for his car, Zeke eyed Dennis Murphy.

"Mike pegged you right as a Dennis-the-Menace character," Zeke said. "Your dad should have held out longer on you having a car—say until you were twenty-eight instead of eighteen—and had some sense!"

It was next day that the full impact of the wild ride struck Zeke. Bob Naffing sent word for him to report to the main office. Zeke's pulse leaped ten beats when he entered and saw a Georgia State Trooper with Naffing.

The officer surveyed Zeke, nodded at Naffing. "He's the feller I saw leaving town last night in a convertible *like* the one I'd chased for twenty miles, if it wasn't the same," the trooper said.

"This officer has been more than fair, Pender," Naffing said. "There won't be any ticket, no charges will be filed. Something went wrong with his radio, and he couldn't contact ahead; he isn't positive it was you and your car. He thinks there were two in the car he chased. I ask you just one question: were you in Waycross and Blackshear and Hoboken and back to Waycross last night?"

Things flashed through Zeke's mind in kaleidoscopic pattern. The most prominent piece in the pattern was labeled *I haven't got a driver's license yet!* Another was *no charges will be filed.* He said, "Yes, sir, I was."

Bob Naffing eyed him, shook his head, then said to the officer, "We appreciate your cooperation."

After the trooper left, Naffing regarded Zeke frowningly. "I have a vague recollection of you and Murphy leaving camp in your car last night," he said. "Today Murphy is sporting a new convertible. Is there anything you'd care to add to the picture?"

"No, sir."

Naffing again regarded the youth. Finally he said, "All right, the matter's closed. It looks as though Murphy isn't alone in needing to grow up!"

9: *West Palm Beach Again—But Different*

SOMEBODY SAW ZEKE come from the tepee in which Naffing's office was located, shortly after the state trooper drove out of the camp. A garbled and fictitious story spread around. By the time Dennis Murphy heard it, Zeke Pender was as good as in jail already. Murphy sought out his roommate.

"This thing about a cop being out here after you—give!" Murphy demanded.

"There's nothing to give. There was a state trooper here, yes. I suppose you could say he was after me, in a way. But—"

"It was about last night, wasn't it!" Murphy broke in on Zeke, then did not wait for confirmation. "You can't take the grief for me! I'm going to Naffing and lay the whole thing on the line. He can call the cops, and I'll swallow my medicine!"

Zeke gripped Murphy's arm. "You'll do nothing of the sort. Listen!"

He told Murphy the facts. "Nothing would be gained," he finished. "Naffing said the matter was closed. Forget all this, and concentrate on the thing we're here for!"

"That crack you handed me about Dad should have made me wait another ten years wasn't so far off." Murphy's tone expressed self-disgust. "I acted like a juvenile delinquent!"

"Right." Zeke nodded agreement. "And the next time you get off on a smart-aleck kid slant, old Zeke just might turn you over his knee. So watch it!"

The full schedule of work made time go rapidly for Zeke. He always scanned the bulletin board, and one morning he was actually startled at a placard some wag had posted.

Final Week, Last Chance. Change For Austin, Yakima, West Palm Beach And Way Points!

"It's hard to realize," Zeke told Denny. "It doesn't seem as though we've been here more than a week!"

"That's what *you* say! For me, Naffing and Company have been riding me for a month of Sundays!"

"I think you make a big deal out of things just to keep in practice in case something comes along that rates it," Zeke said. "Okay, say that Naffing and Mike and other coaches have borne down on you. You needed it, and you're a lot better pitcher for the extra time they spent with you!"

"Speaking of extra time, Naffing and Oldham have sure given you the works lately. Something special coming up?"

"I never give things like that a thought, as long as—" Zeke broke off and grinned sheepishly. "I'd be lying if I pretended I hadn't noticed. But I honestly have no idea whether anything special is coming. Anyway, what could come up special?"

"They could be getting you set for a trip down to West Palm so you'll get acquainted with the big club before you start north with them!"

"Something like that's been bugging me." Zeke nodded, going along with Murphy's fantasy. "It would make it awful tough for you fellows to get along up here. Well, you'd just have to make do. Mike warned you that professional baseball is a rough, dog-eat-dog proposition."

Zeke and his roommate laughed. But the rookie catcher did not laugh when Bob Naffing came to Tepee Two that night and instructed Zeke to be prepared to leave early next morning.

"We'll drive to Jacksonville and grab a plane that will get us to West Palm Beach three hours before game time."

Zeke stared, stunned. He knew that Bob Naffing did not joke about such matters, but there was something that wasn't just right. It was not too hard to figure what it was, since he read everything he found in sport sheets about the Atlanta Braves' Grapefruit League games. He said, "Aren't the Braves on a swing through Gulf Coast training camps for games with the Pirates, White Sox, Mets, and Cardinals?"

"Right, and the B club is playing University of Miami a series of games while the A club is away."

Naffing, after giving Zeke a speculative look, said as though to himself, "May help him to know the score." Then he continued, "You've looked very good up here. You're improving right along, and our reports to the Farm Director have noted your progress. You're to catch tomorrow's game for the B squad. Evidently the powers that be want a personal look at you."

Naffing did not identify "the powers that be." Zeke did not think it would make any difference to him if the General Manager, the Farm Director and even the Field Manager of the Braves—Skipper, to men under him—were watching. A ballgame was a ballgame.

This one became a nightmare for Zeke Pender.

The starting pitcher for the Braves was wild. He walked the first Miami U. batter on four pitches, all the way out of the strike zone. He plunked a slow curve into the ribs of the second man to come to the plate. Zeke signed to the umpire for the time and started toward the mound with the ball. The pitcher took two steps toward home plate, held out his glove and snarled, "The ball! That's all I want from you. Just get back of the dish and start calling some right stuff!"

Zeke stared. The pitcher had not yet thrown a ball anywhere near where it had been called, but this was a fellow who had finished the previous season with the National League Braves. He had been tabbed by sportswriters as a fine addition to the pitching staff—providing he solved his control problem.

The rookie catcher shrugged, tossed the pitcher the ball, and said nothing. He returned to his position and crouched behind the batter and signed for a fast ball down the inside edge of the plate.

It was not a fast ball and it was far from being down the inside edge. Whether he misread the sign, the pitcher broke off a sweeping curve. Not a wild pitch, the ball was very wide, and Zeke had been crossed up. He stabbed his glove out, but merely slowed the sphere's course to the wall in front of the stands. Baserunners advanced to third and second. The public address horns blared the official scorer's decision: "A passed ball."

Zeke never understood what the pitcher could have been thinking as he toed the pitching rubber and faced the batter—he took a full windup. But runners were alert. The man from third was no more than five strides from the plate when the ball left the pitcher's hand. Instead of being inside as Zeke had signed, the pitch was again wide. There was no chance either to get the man sliding across the plate or to make a play on the runner from second sliding into third.

Miami U. scored four runs that first inning without the benefit of a solid hit, but the wild pitcher finished the inning.

A new pitcher was on the mound when the Braves took the field in the second inning. Three more worked for the B club that day. Miami players totaled eleven runs. The collegians stole three bases. Zeke Pender was charged with two more passed balls. B club infielders committed four errors, and there were two bad throwing errors by outfielders.

Zeke hit deep to left center his first time at bat. A fine running catch retired him. In three other appearances at the plate, the rookie hit sharply into a double play, was fooled by a good change-up and popped to shortstop, and drove the left fielder to the fence before he dragged down a solidly hit drive.

"It was the poorest game I ever played, bar none." Zeke shuddered the next day as he recounted the horrible details to Dennis Murphy. "It was terrible—I mean, *I* was terrible!"

"Oh-for-four at the platter and three passed balls sure doesn't sound like a Zeke Pender day. You were trying too hard, too tightened up."

"Naffing didn't have anything like that to say." Zeke shook his head. "He laid it right on the line—I was responsible for the team falling apart, because I didn't tell off that pitcher instead of letting him shove me around!"

"Why *didn't* you read him off and take charge, Zeke?"

"Gosh, how's a fellow like me going to read off a big league pitcher!"

"Easy." Dennis Murphy eyed his roommate. "I had a catcher walk out and tell me once if I didn't calm down and start pitching where he called 'em, he'd heave the apple down my throat! Wise up, that's all you need. You're going to be a big leaguer. Start practicing to act like one!"

"I might better practice acting like the rawest rookie assigned to a rookie league club. That's what I'll be after yesterday—if they don't pay off the rest of my contract and send me back to the factory league!"

Bob Naffing was called to the Braves' Atlanta office the day before players were assigned to various farm clubs in the Braves system. Mike Oldham gave Zeke the news of his assignment.

"You're going back to West Palm Beach," Mike said. "You and Murphy. I'll be with you. They're making me comanager down there. Now, get this straight—neither you nor Murphy should be disappointed. You'll be Number One catcher, and you'll work 'most every game. Murphy will pitch in our starting rotation. You'll both get more experience than you would by sitting on the bench for a Double or Triple A outfit.

"And one big thing to keep in mind is that players can be called up to the Big Time from a Class A club!"

10 : *New Season, New Home*

MUNICIPAL STADIUM, home of the West Palm Beach Braves now that the major leaguers had gone, seemed different to Zeke. He checked the stands, the scoreboard, the high green wall behind the fence in center field that gave batters a fine background, the flag pole in left center field. There was no physical change.

"But there's a difference somewhere," he said to Dennis Murphy. They reached the left field bullpen for pregame warmup. "It kind of bugs me, because I can't spot it."

"Looks the same to me." Murphy threw easily to Zeke from halfway to the mound. "I won't need many loosening tosses. My arm already feels loose, it's such a swell, warm night."

"Night! That's what's different." Zeke grinned.

"We didn't play night games in the Instructional League, and that horrible thing with Miami University was a day game."

"Okay, that's settled." Murphy toed a pitcher's slab on the bullpen mound. "A few fast ones, a curve or two, and some change-ups will do it."

The slender southpaw signaled he felt ready to pitch before the infield workout was done. Zeke took over the plate duties for the final rounds. Then a voice spoke over the public address system.

"Introducing the West Palm Beach Braves: Dan Meyer, Number Seven, first base."

The player called trotted from the dugout and stood along the third base line near the plate. The p.a. voice called off the rest of the starting team, then the pitchers and utility men that made up the seventeen-player Braves roster. Mike Oldham and his comanager jogged from the dugout last.

The entire visiting club—Cocoa Beach Astros, farm club of the Houston Astros—came out and stood along the first base foul line. A record player filled the night air with the strains of *The Star Spangled Banner* while players and umpires stood at attention.

"And now, the Mayor of West Palm Beach will throw out the first ball. You may fire when ready, Your Honor, and the Florida State League season will be officially open."

The Mayor stood in the box in the stands next to the Braves dugout, posed while a news photographer's camera bulb flashed, then made a very creditable throw that Zeke caught near the plate. The rookie catcher trotted to the box and asked the mayor to autograph the brand-new baseball. The city official wrote his name on the horsehide. Then he surprised Zeke.

A motion to Mike Oldham brought another ball tossed from the comanager and caught by the mayor. He handed the sphere to Zeke, along with his pen.

"I want *your* autograph." His Honor smiled. "When you're a big league star I can boast that I knew you when you were just breaking into pro baseball. Make it Zeke Pender. My son watched you catch a couple of games last fall and you're currently his idol and model."

Zeke wrote his name on the ball. Teammates kidded him. "May I have your autograph sometime? . . . Good thing the mayor didn't autograph your cap, you'd never have got it back on! . . . You would'a had a battle to catch that onion if I'd known there was a chance to get a fan club organized! . . . Man, you have to produce a hot night, now, for the mayor and his kid!"

Both Zeke and his roommate produced hot nights.

The Braves southpaw gave up but two hits, had complete control of Astro batters from the first pitch. He issued no walks, his teammates gave him faultless support in the field, and nothing but zeroes went on the scoreboard in the *Visitors* line.

Zeke came to bat in the bottom of the third, two teammates on base. He drove a hit to left center field to score the first run of the game. In the bottom of the eighth, the rookie catcher endeared himself to Braves fans. A teammate was on first when Zeke took his third turn at the plate. A two-and-two pitch came up there a little inside but too close to take. Zeke swung merely to protect the plate. The result showed the raw power in the youngster's hitting ability. It was not a line drive, but the towering fly dropped over the fence to the center field side of the 395 marker.

Dennis Murphy set down Astro batters one-two-three in their ninth. Mike Oldham hurried from the dugout to meet the lefthander, grabbed his hand and slapped his shoulder. Then Mike slapped Zeke on the seat of the pants.

You called a beautiful game," Mike said, "and two-for-four at the dish is more than all right." Mike's eyes sparkled then as he added, "Three ribbies every game would make you all-time champ in any league!"

Zeke felt warm and good as he left the clubhouse. Nothing was further from his mind than what came about. "Zeke! Can you spare a moment or two?" A voice called.

The surprise at hearing his name was increased when Zeke saw the caller was the gray-haired gentleman at whose home he had watched a World Series game with Bob Naffing.

"Why, Mr. Murphy!" Zeke stopped and his eyes widened. "Migosh," he said, "I actually hadn't thought about Dennis Murphy and you bearing the same name! It couldn't be you're related!"

"I don't quite understand," Mr. Murphy said.

Dennis Murphy came from the clubhouse, glanced at Zeke and the elderly gentleman, and started toward his convertible in the parking lot. Zeke grabbed his roommate's arm.

"Meet a grand gentleman," Zeke said. "Mr. Murphy, my roommate, Dennis Murphy. That's what struck me just now, your names."

"Nice to meet you, son." Mr. Murphy eyed the lefthander as they shook hands. "You pitched great ball, big league ball. It would please me if I could claim relationship, but if any exists, it must be generations back. I'm the only descendant of my branch of Murphys to emigrate from Ireland."

The white-haired gentleman turned to Zeke. "Mrs. Murphy and I have been on a boat cruise around the Bahamas," he said. "Bob Naffing answered my inquiry about you and wrote you'd be with our club, but I had no opportunity to contact you. We only returned late this afternnon. There are two questions, Zeke. I hope you will answer both in the affirmative.

"First: will you make your base at our place while the club is home? We have a large room going unused. Mrs. Murphy and I would greatly appreciate having you live with us. The second question is: will you drive me home? Or at least into town where I can get a cab."

Zeke did not hesitate. "You're very kind, sir, and I certainly will take advantage of your invitation. Dennis and I are rooming at Town House, but only on a weekly basis."

"Does that mean you might be induced to come along with Zeke, son?" Mr. Murphy eyed Dennis Murphy. "Having two youngsters around would knock years and years off my missus and myself!"

Dennis looked at Zeke, said, "I don't get this. You've never said anything about having friends or relatives or anybody down here."

Zeke explained how he happened to know Mr. Murphy. At the end, Dennis said enthusiastically, "It sounds great. We can store one car."

"We have a two-car garage," Mr. Murphy said. "And I no longer maintain an automobile. My second question was: will you drive me home, or at least into West Palm where I can get a cab?"

"Mr. Murphy," Dennis said, "in addition to acquiring two roomers, you also have from now on two convertibles, complete with drivers."

They drove the elderly gentleman to Juno Beach, left Zeke's car there. On the way back to West Palm, Dennis Murphy let out a breath. "What a night!", he said. "A two-hit shutout for my first pro start, and finding a swell gent like Mr. Murphy."

"He's not only a wonderful guy but a real knowledgeable baseball fan," Zeke said. "Maybe you noticed that his comments and questions about the game tonight were right in the groove?"

"How could a ballplayer miss noticing? If the Braves can be in the groove as much as Mr. Murphy, we won't lose a game!"

11 : A Homer and A No-hitter

THE BRAVES WERE "in the groove" the next night against the Astros. The starting pitcher went all the way, allowed seven scattered hits, but only two runs. His teammates battered Cocoa pitching for nine runs.

The Fort Lauderdale Yankees came into Municipal Stadium. A third member of the West Palm Beach pitching staff turned in a complete game. Braves, 6: Yankees, 4. Dennis Murphy baffled Yankee batters for seven innings of his second mound turn. They got to him for three hits in the eighth. Combined with a fielder's choice and a sacrifice fly the trio of safeties accounted for the Yankee runs in a fifth consecutive win for the Braves, 8-3.

The club went on the road, won two in Miami, two

in Daytona Beach, and took the first of a two-game series scheduled for Tampa's Al Lang Field.

"Ten straight!" Mike Oldham smiled blissfully that night in the clubhouse. "Man, do I *love* that third base coaching spot!"

A sportswriter was interviewing Zeke, trying to pry a story out of the league's RBI leader—9 in ten games—and one of the .400 hitters in the young season. The newspaperman said, "What's liking to coach at third have to do with winning ten straight?"

"Our managers set it up so that one would be manager and the other coach. The one who was manager would be third base coach, the other first base coach. They'd change whenever the club lost. Mike won the toss to start as manager, and he's been coaching at third all during our winning streak."

"Did you flip a coin with other guys to see who'd carry the biggest bat?"

"No, sir, nothing like that." Zeke laughed.

"Do you figure you'll maintain a .400 batting average? Do you expect to maintain your RBI pace? How long can the club keep winning?"

"Until we lose." Zeke grinned. "Our streak is bound to end. I've been lucky in having hits drop in. One of these nights I may be just as unlucky and everything I knock will be grabbed for an out. It would be fine with me if I could hit .300 right along."

Rain washed out the second game at Tampa, and St. Petersburg washed out the Braves winning streak the next night. A pitcher failed for the first time to last. The sad fact was that relievers who came from the bullpen also failed to last. St. Pete batters sprayed fourteen base hits all over the field and used a couple of walks and an error to make them produce twelve runs.

Zeke's consecutive hitting streak continued, but he had no RBI in the 12-5 loss.

"It just doesn't seem right." Dennis Murphy complained after he threw a five-hit, 6-2 win against St. Petersburg the next night.

Mike Oldham shook his head. "How about this wrong-armer?" he asked. "He wins three straight and gripes that something isn't right."

"I wasn't talking about me," Murphy said quickly. Then he seemed suddenly embarrassed. "I—what I meant was it seems as though we ought to have more than a measly half-game lead, winning eleven of twelve."

Mike Oldham regarded the young southpaw pitcher and said, "Rack one against me. I'm sorry. The way it looks from as far as we've gone, this league is well balanced. Sarasota's breathing down our necks and Orlando's only a game back of them. Leesburg's won six straight after dropping four of their first five. The Yankees are beginning to jell. Miami comes up with another good starting pitcher, so they'll be tough. Four or five teams could battle right down to the wire for the first-half championship."

The race continued exceptionally close as April gave way to May. Mr. Murphy summed things up neatly when the Braves won their final game in May.

"Hitters hit, pitchers pitch, fielders are turning in better defensive play than you might expect in Class A ball," he said. "Our club rates being four or five games or more out in front. But Sarasota and St. Pete and Tampa have been getting hitting, pitching, and fine defensive play. You fellows can be well satisfied if you're one game ahead at the end."

Going into June the Braves had a record of thirty wins and fifteen losses. They maintained the same rip-roaring .750 pace through June—but with only a game at Cocoa left on the first-half schedule, the West Palm Beach Braves needed either a win or a Sarasota loss to keep from being tied.

Mike Oldham and his fellow manager had manipulated pitching assignments so that Dennis Murphy was rested for the important game.

"Murphy's beaten this club three times, and they've made only fifteen hits off his stuff," Mike said in the pregame clubhouse meeting. "But percentages have a way of catching up in baseball. We can't afford to let down a bit and have this be the night percentages catch us! Bear down from the start, everybody hustle all the time!"

Mike stopped Zeke as the catcher walked from the clubhouse. "As one catcher to another," Mike said, "this has to be your game as much as Murphy's—maybe more. You've got a book on these guys. Keep Murphy in line; he's only a kid, and the pressure just could get to him."

"We've gone over the batters together," Zeke said. "Denny won't give us any trouble. I don't think he's the kind to crack under pressure."

Murphy was sharp when he warmed up. Then as he worked on the leadoff batter the lefthander seemed to have left his sharpness in the bullpen. He labored hard, got a three-and-one count, then lost his man. Dennis Murphy stood and stared at the umpire.

Zeke called time and clumped out to the mound.

"Easy does it," Zeke warned. "It was so close that the batter wouldn't have squawked if it had been ruled a strike. But the umpire said ball, and you can't afford to let it bug you. Keep 'em down on this next guy and we'll make him hit a double-play ball."

If the batter had swung at the next pitch, there would have been more probability of a two-base hit rather than a double play. Zeke recognized instantly when the ball left Murphy's hand that he was off stride. Fortunately the batter did not offer at the curve that hung at the top of the strike zone, a foot higher than Zeke had called.

The umpire decided it was a ball. Murphy charged from the mound, mouth open, clearly intending to jaw at the umpire.

Zeke turned and said, "Time!" to the umpire. He ran three steps toward Murphy and barked, "Shut up!"

He reached the pitcher and shoved him back toward the mound and turned him facing away from the umpire.

"So it was another border-line call. You're not helping any by beefing," Zeke said.

"That Blind Tom ought to get a tin cup and a seeing-eye dog! He can't—"

"Shut up!" Zeke gripped Murphy's arm. "You remember telling me about a catcher who threatened to heave the ball down your throat? And I told you once that if you ever got off on a smart-alecky slant I'd turn you over my knee? Well, I'll bust the ball down your throat harder than that other catcher threatened. Then I'll paddle you right out here, so help me! Pay attention, now."

DER
17

"You've lost your rhythm. You're letting pressure get you, worse than I did when I caught for the B club. Okay, get mad; maybe it'll help as long as you're mad at me or yourself. But get back on that slab and pump and cut loose as you were doing in the warm-ups. Starting right now!"

Zeke held his roommate's gaze. Murphy glared, then dropped his eyes. "Starting right now," he said, "you're the hot shot! You sign for 'em, and I'll bust 'em up there where you call 'em—and you'd better be right!"

Dennis Murphy retired the Astros without further threat. The batter rapped into a double play, slapping a low breaking curve to the second baseman, a perfect ground ball near the bag, which shortened the toss to shortstop for the force and gave him time to avoid a sliding runner and get off his relay to first.

The third batter fell victim to a deceptive change-up that Zeke called for strike three.

It was the sixth inning when Zeke began thinking about a possible no-hitter. Other Braves must have been thinking along the same line. In the dugout there was a strained and elaborate effort toward no-mention of the hit situation for the Astros.

Dennis Murphy made hash of the old superstition after setting down Astro batters in order to complete the seventh inning.

"Get some runs, you guys," he said when he came into the dugout. "Do you expect a chucker to throw a no-hitter and then finally lose it because he doesn't get one measly run to work on?"

No runs were scored by the Braves in the top of the eighth. Two routine ground balls to infielders and an easy fly to center field disposed of the Astros in their eighth.

Zeke Pender led off the ninth for the Braves. Before he left the dugout, Zeke received a pep talk from his roommate.

"Get hold of one," Dennis Murphy said. "Get on. I'll bunt you ahead a base and Dick or Dan'll knock you on around."

Zeke said, "This pitcher slipped and laid one in my groove last time I faced him. Maybe he'll slip again."

Mike Oldham stopped at the lip of the dugout before going to the third base coach's box. "You've got the green light to go after anything that looks good to you, Zeke," Mike said. "Nail one!"

Zeke "nailed" the first pitch. Every ounce of power his wide shoulders could generate was behind the swing. The thick part of the bat collided squarely with the speeding ball. The drive was a home run from the moment the ball left the bat on a sharply rising trajectory. It cleared the left field fence by more than ten feet. That solo home run proved to be the ballgame.

In the bottom of the ninth Zeke Pender was more interested in getting Astro batters out without a hit than in anything else. He was careful to go back in his mental "book" on each hitter before he signed for the pitch he wanted.

Murphy had been getting batters out all night with his change-up, but Zeke recalled that the man the southpaw faced for the final out was not easily fooled. Also, he was not a really good fast-ball hitter.

Zeke signed for a fast ball, along the outside edge of the strike zone. It seemed to him that Murphy hesitated overlong, and Zeke straightened, gave the pitcher a look, settled again, and made the same sign.

The fast ball came, and the batter took it. Strike one. Zeke called for the same pitch. Strike two. Now the batter would be guarding the plate, but he might not expect a third fast ball, and he still was not a good fast-ball hitter. Zeke signed for a third fireball down the outside edge. The batter swung late, missed.

Three out, a no-hit game for Murphy—and the first-half championship for the West Palm Beach Braves!

12 : In a Slump

"First-half champs!" Mike Oldham's tone dripped disgust. "First-half *chumps* is more like it! What happened to you guys?"

Somebody in the back of the clubhouse muttered, "How about Murphy being moved to Austin and upsetting things?"

"Bunk!" Mike Oldham snorted. "Somewhere along the line you guys have had it jammed down your throats that this pro baseball is a *profession.* Professional people advance as they get better. Murphy's record even without the no-hitter rated a move to a higher classification. How would it have been if the front office had moved Pender and Cook and Brown up? They rated it. I suppose then you would have dropped clear through the bottom into a rookie league!"

The long-time former player in the Braves organization glared around the group.

"We're in the fifth week of the second half of the split schedule," he said. "We're running a lousy last in the standings. Fans are beginning to wonder whether we're playing patty-cake so we'll get into a playoff with the second-half winners. Nobody in the Braves organization wants that. We have the best club in this league. We've got to get along!"

Zeke Pender was fully aware that Mike Oldham held his gaze at the end of his exhortation. The awareness did nothing toward helping the rookie catcher out of the gloom he had been wallowing in for what seemed forever. Mike asked him to wait a minute when he dismissed the meeting.

Visitors, 8; Braves, 3. The scoreboard picture after that night's game was vivid in Zeke's thoughts. Mike Oldham did not beat around the bush.

"Bob Naffing told you long ago that in the Braves organization there is no hesitation in placing the finger of blame for a club falling apart," Mike said. "It's on the catcher. Taking it from there, I have a legitimate right to put the finger on you. Our trouble doesn't stem from the collapse of our defense, but the guilt-finger still points at you, Zeke."

Mike Oldham regarded the rookie catcher a long moment. His tone was that of a friend rather than a manager when he spoke again.

"What goes with you?" he asked. "I thought I knew you pretty well. I was sure that you wouldn't be shook when the Atlanta brass moved Murphy to Austin. Don't forget that Naffing promoted me to this job primarily to work with you. I have no beef about your development as a catcher."

The comanager of the West Palm Beach Braves frowned.

"But I do have a beef," he said. "You're ruining our ballclub because you aren't hitting. Why it is that a gang of ballplayers rear and tear or fold up according to the way one player goes, I'll never understand, but that's the way it is. Right now it would not be a mis-statement to put it that as Zeke Pender goes, so go the West Palm Beach Braves!"

Zeke looked as miserable as he felt. He said, "Mike, I'll do anything you say. I don't know what's happened to me. I'm oh-for-twenty-nine. I'm wondering if I could *buy* a hit. I've never gone to bat twenty-nine times before without getting my share of base hits."

"Have you ever heard of a slump, Zeke? You're in a slump at the plate, and the whole blamed club has slumped along with you! What have you done before to pull yourself out of a slump?"

"Nothing. I've heard of slumps, of course. But I've never experienced one—until now."

Mike Oldham again regarded the rookie, and finally said, "Welcome to the lodge. You may well be the only ballplayer wearing the monkey suit of a pro club who could make that statement."

"How do you go about getting out of a slump, Mike?"

"Good question." Mike Oldham nodded. "If I could give a solution guaranteed to work, I'd be the greatest ever. Sooner or later—and too often, sometimes—

slumps come to every ballplayer. There are oodles of things hitters have tried to break slumps."

Zeke said, "You've been in slumps, Mike. What did you do?"

"Well, a guy like me never could slump very much. A fielder's choice, an error, a bloop hit over the infield, or a leg hit beating a throw from deep short was a hitting streak for me. But I have made a study of slumps.

"All the great hitters from Willie Keeler and Dan Brouthers and Ty Cobb to Mickey Mantle and Willie Mays—right down to whoever leads the National League and the American League in batting this year —they've all gone through maddening slumps."

Mike Oldham shook his head.

"Slumps creep up on you. You're going great guns, clobbering everything the pitchers serve. Suddenly your drives are going straight at fielders. Nothing drops in safely. At first it doesn't bother you. You wonder how lucky pitchers can get, the same chuckers you've been belting all over the lot.

"Pretty soon it begins to get worse, because nothing you hit goes right. You're puzzled and maybe a little concerned, but not really worried. Then maybe somebody in the dugout, or a sportswriter, says something about a slump. Not you! You'll show 'em. So you begin pressing at the plate—and you're worse off than ever."

Mike shrugged.

"You finally reach a point of desperation where you've tried everything anyone suggests. You become convinced that you never were a real hitter. So, what the heck! You relax, take things calm and cool. Then you belt a safe hit, and you're out of your slump."

Mike looked at the rookie catcher and a note of pleading came into the tone of the Braves comanager.

"Try to relax and get back on the beam," he said. "Whether you ever hit another homer or drive in another run, we need the threat of your bat. Pitchers are taking liberties with us that they wouldn't take if you were hitting. Please get with it, Zeke!"

Zeke tried. It may have been that he tried too hard. His frustration at the plate continued. It was in the first game of a double-header at Daytona Beach that he broke his hit famine. The official scorer was generous, gave him credit for two hits, but Zeke discounted one to deep short that he barely beat out because it was bobbled.

Neither of the "hits" counted in run production.

In the second game he tried bunting. The net result was howling jeers from the fans at his slow-footedness.

The club returned to Municipal Stadium from Daytona. Zeke was up early the next morning. He walked the beach. Near the fishing pier he saw a pelican struggling to get air-borne with the discarded carcass of a filleted kingfish in its beak. Idly Zeke watched the clumsy-appearing bird.

The pelican failed and failed and failed, but the bird never gave up. He just kept attacking the carcass from different positions. Finally the pelican seemed to crouch on top of a wave breaking over the bar, then leaped at the carcass of the kingfish. The bird rode the breaker a few yards and managed to get into the air with its burden.

That night Zeke Pender failed to produce on two

occasions when he came to bat with mates on the bases. The Braves lost, 5-4.

Mrs. Murphy surprised Zeke at breakfast the next morning. She said, "I have the recipe for a wonderful cake for your birthday dinner tomorrow, Claude."

It always took Zeke a fraction of time to realize that Mrs. Murphy was addressing him. She simply refused to call him Zeke. "Vulgar!" she would sniff. "The boy's name is Claude!"

This day he said, "Ma'am?" and was abruptly aware that Mr. Murphy had delivered a healthy kick against his shin. Zeke hid a wince, said, "Oh! Yes'm."

Mrs. Murphy went to the kitchen for something. Mr. Murphy whispered fiercely, "Go along with her! She knows it isn't your birthday, but she has a theory that a celebration will relax you and get you—well, Mother puts it 'free and easy.' She maintains that what you need is to get your mind off baseball, so to speak, and just swing that bat and you'll begin hitting."

Mr. Murphy glanced toward the kitchen, then went on hurriedly. "She also thinks you're standing too far from the plate and using a stance that's too open."

That night as he warmed up the starting pitcher, Zeke was thinking of other things: the pelican that had tried different ways until success came; Mrs. Murphy camouflaging her concern yet handing out sage advice.

His first time at bat, Zeke closed his stance a bit. He stood a little deeper in the batter's box. He intended to keep trying different things. Maybe he could come up with a pelican-inspired-slump-getter-out-of, with an assist from Mrs. Murphy.

He drove a clean hit over second base on the third

pitch. Exultation leaped through him, but Zeke reserved judgment. The second time he came to the plate, a teammate was on first base. Zeke hit the ball hard. The second baseman made a diving stop of the sharp grounder and turned it into a force-out at second.

Two mates were on base when Zeke came to bat in the sixth inning. Zeke hit a long fly to deep center field. Both runners advanced, but gloom held Zeke as he returned to the dugout.

Apprehension as well as gloom came to the rookie when he saw Mike Oldham donning shin guards and chest protector. He looked out at third base. The co-manager had taken over there. A utility infielder was in the coach's box behind first base.

"Good thing I cleared myself with the league office to be reactivated as a player," Mike said. "You're to report to the office right away, Zeke. I'll take over the catching."

Zeke stared at the coach speechless, then dropped his eyes.

Well, you couldn't really expect they'd go along indefinitely with a guy who hasn't hit his weight for five weeks, he thought. *About the best I can hope for is to be sent to a rookie league club, instead of getting a ticket back home.*

PART THREE

Atlanta Braves Rookie

13 : A Stunned Rookie Catcher

THE OFFICE OF the general manager of the West Palm Beach Braves was about midway between the Braves clubhouse and the clubhouse of the visiting club. Zeke walked more and more slowly, but he knew that stalling would not change whatever was in store for him.

He pushed open the door. He expected to see the round face of Hank Stein, the general manager. Instead it was Bob Naffing who looked up sharply from behind the desk.

"It's about time you showed," Naffing said. "Hank let me use his office. Go shower, get dressed in a hurry and clean out your locker. I've contacted the Murphys. It's a break they were entertaining friends so they stayed home tonight. They'll have a bag packed with your toilet articles and a change of stuff. We'll drive out and get the bag and say good-bye to them. There won't be too much leeway, but we should be able to make it back to the airport before your plane leaves. Before I forget, take charge of these."

Naffing put a key and a business card into an envelope marked with the name of an airline. He handed the envelope to Zeke.

"Take a cab from the Atlanta airport to the address I've written on the back of the card," Naffing said. "My apartment is 3A, and the key opens the front door. You'll have time to grab a few hours' sleep before the alarm goes off. It's set so you'll get out of the sack in plenty of time tomorow morning."

Zeke nodded. He said gloomily, "They didn't want to hand Hank the job of tomahawking me. I get it."

"You get what? And that tomahawking crack—what are you talking about?"

"Me being sent back to factory league ball."

Naffing eyed the big rookie for a moment, then made a little gesture. "I'm sorry," he said. "Things have been moving pretty fast. I haven't clued you yet. You're to report by ten tomorrow morning to the Skipper. He'll be in his office off the Atlanta Braves clubhouse at the Stadium. The guard at the ramp where the cab stops can direct you."

"Did—did you say report to the Skipper? You—you mean the manager of the big club?"

"Right. Look, Zeke, we're pressed for time. I'll fill you in while we drive to Juno Beach and back to the airport."

The words that Naffing had poured out were still whirling in Zeke's thoughts after he was on the plane bound for Atlanta.

"Danberro is not a young man . . . needs rest whenever Skipper can give it to him . . . double-headers piling up . . . Danberro just might wear out completely. . . . Collision at the plate yesterday ruined our first reserve catcher. . . . You don't recover from a shoulder separation in a couple of days. . . . Some decisions that have been hanging fire brought to a boil . . . One of them was to bring you up to the big club. . . . That's all you need to know for now."

Zeke's thoughts had still not settled down as he prepared for bed. He was full of questions that Naffing had left unanswered. He doubted that he would ever get to sleep.

He was asleep in less than a minute after pulling up a sheet against the almost-chill of the air conditioning. The buzzing of the electric alarm confused him for a few seconds. Then, as full realization penetrated the fog of half-consciousness, he bounded from bed.

It couldn't have been ringing too long, he thought. It's only eight-fifteen, but I'd better get organized.

He waited outside the door of the manager's office until his watch showed a minute before ten. He wondered whether he was supposed to knock, then decided that a rookie had better.

A voice inside said, "Come on in. It's not locked."

Zeke entered. He recognized the stocky man who rose from a desk at the end of the room. He had seen the manager of the Atlanta Braves on television, leaving the dugout and walking slowly to the mound when a Braves pitcher was in trouble. But the Skipper surprised Zeke.

"Pender," he said. "Have a seat."

"Mr. Naffing told me to report to you by ten, sir," Zeke said.

"And you're on time." He indicated a chair, and Zeke sat. The rookie could not help noticing the neat pile of yellow papers on the desk. They were about five inches by eight inches. *Individual Player Report* was lettered across the top sheet. "Reports on you," Skipper said. "Consistently good, from Naffing back in camp at Waycross and from Oldham since you've been at West Palm Beach."

Then the manager again surprised Zeke. He said, "How do you rate your progress, Pender?"

"Why—why I don't know. I've learned a lot about catching and hitting. I'm still learning about what Mike Oldham calls battery strategy."

"You'll be 'still learning' as long as you're catching." Skipper nodded. "A real pro never stops learning."

The manager looked at Zeke a moment, as though weighing things in his mind.

"You have great potential," he said finally. "I watched you catch a game for our B club last spring. Naffing told me afterward that you felt as though you'd set back any chance of advancing in our system. The way you reacted that day and kept battling against breaks you had no control over convinced me that Naffing's judgment was sound. I was rooting hard for the second ball you got hold of at the plate to clear the fence.

"I like to have a look at a player when he doesn't know he's being scouted. Usually I have a ball, and that day was more fun than usual. I sat in the right field bleachers, wore sunglasses and a wide-brimmed hat, and nobody recognized me. Needling and arguments always come up among bleacher fans, and I was right in there on everything that went on around me."

The outside door of the clubhouse opened. Bob Naffing said, "Okay if I come in, Skipper?"

"Sure." The Braves manager looked surprised. "How'd you get here so soon? Didn't you tell me you'd be driving Pender's car up?"

"I found out when I got back to Juno Beach that a neighbor of our friend down there is as much a football buff as Murphy is a baseball fan. He and his wife and son are driving to Chicago to see the College All Stars workout and take in the big All Star-Professional game at Soldier's Field. The boy was tickled to grab a few bucks to drive Zeke's car to Atlanta. I flew out of West Palm Beach this morning."

Relief showed on the Skipper's tanned face, and it was in his tone when he spoke. "Things are working out as though we'd planned them that way," he said. "The Front Office was on the phone not five minutes before Pender came. A deal we've been working on is coming to a head, and I've made it clear that I want to be in on any final decision."

The Braves manager opened a drawer of his desk and took out a typed sheet.

"You show Pender around," he said to Naffing. "I'll be upstairs if you want me for anything."

Bob Naffing nodded, caught Zeke's eye, and headed for the door from the manager's room into the clubhouse.

Zeke remembered long afterward the thrill that came to him when he entered the clubhouse. He could see through the door to the shower room. Eight shower heads were on opposite walls, each at the end of a jointed, adjustable arm. Everything was tiled and spotlessly clean. The door to the trainer's room was open, and he could see training tables and a whirlpool bath.

"You can see," Naffing said, "we have the best of accommodations."

Lockers bearing the players' names ranged along each side of the clubhouse and across the front. Each one had ventilated sides, a shelf with three compartments, and a rod with several clothes hangers. A storage compartment across the locker had its cover at proper height for a seat.

"The ramp to the dugout is down here," Naffing said. Zeke followed him. Naffing indicated the rubber matting on the floor of the ramp. "Concrete dulls spikes," he said.

There were two drinking fountains on the landing at the bottom of the ramp. A helmet rack with sixteen compartments was at the home-plate end of the dugout, and a card with a batting order was taped to the wall above the dugout bench. Zeke thought it must be the batting order for last night's game.

The bat rack was also at the home-plate end of the dugout. Each compartment of the rack bore the name of a team member.

A step-high platform held the players' bench with its comfortable backrest slatted like the seat. Four fluorescent-light cylinders were fastened to the ceiling. From the top step of the dugout a dirt path led to the plate.

"Well, there it is." Naffing waved an arm from left

field to right field. "The only stadium in the world anywhere near its size that was built from scratch in just under twelve months. They started it in the spring of 1964, and the Braves and Tigers played a series of exhibition games in April 1965, less than a year later.

"It cost eighteen million dollars: lower deck, narrow middle deck known as the club deck, and an upper deck. It seats 51,000 for baseball. The foul-line markers in left and right are 325 feet from the plate. Left center and right center are 385 feet, and deep center field is 402 feet."

Naffing indicated a bench set back in the wall outside the right-field foul line and another similar bench outside the left-field foul line.

"Bullpen benches," he said. "Two pitcher's mounds and two plates for each bullpen. Cinder track around the entire outfield and a six-foot wire fence about fifteen feet out from the wall of the stands. In my opinion, it is the finest layout in the country." Naffing grinned. "And that includes Houston's wondrous Dome. Tens of thousands of Atlantans agree with me."

Naffing stopped a moment, looked at Zeke, then said, "Any questions?"

"One, king-size. Why me?"

Naffing looked thoughtful and finally nodded. "You want to know why you were brought up instead of a catcher from the Triple A club, or from Austin, or maybe Yakima," he said. "The Braves' main object is to provide winning baseball for Atlanta. Winning teams draw larger crowds and command greater interest, which leads to better television and radio contracts. Let's face it, probaseball is big business. Okay.

"Concede that our top men are realists. They're also square shooters. The controversy over our catching situation has been chiefly in the interest of future Braves ballclubs. Say we made some mistakes: if something can be saved, it's that much to the good. Our general manager has been negotiating for some time for a trade involving a—a—well, between you and me, Manley.

"He's had a fair season at Austin, but if we brought him up now, the trade negotiations might go down the drain. Anyway, the decision that Manley doesn't fit in the picture of future Braves catching is firm. You've never been considered as trade material and the situations with a couple of other young catching prospects are such that bringing them up now might not work out well."

Bob Naffing again looked at Zeke. The rookie got the impression that Naffing was considering whether he should be let in on all the angles. The decision was evidently affirmative.

"The deal being considered for Manley at present gives us a young pitcher and a rookie league outfielder that we believe is a sleeper. There may be other angles the other club is figuring that we don't know, but that doesn't concern us. We simply want to salvage some of the dough we put out to get Manley's signature. The injury to Danberro's backup man has precipitated things.

"Skipper is one of the finest judges of baseball talent in the business. He's been more and more sold on you since he sneaked a personal look, and the reports from Mike Oldham have helped solidify Skipper's opinion. The slump you're just coming out of doesn't perturb him. Skipper wanted you brought up. So-o-o-o, here you are."

Zeke nodded slowly, "A rookie still in stunned shock," he said.

14 : May Not Last— But Great While It Does!

ZEKE PENDER FULLY recognized his rookie status as he came around the front of the batting cage and stepped into the batter's box. But he felt entirely different from the way he had the first time he swung a bat as a professional.

"Cool and easy, Zeke." Bob Naffing spoke in a low tone to the rookie. He was again performing the catching duties for batting practice. "The pitcher up here is the same sixty feet away as in Class A ball, and the mound's the same height. Easy and relaxed does it. You don't have to prove to anyone that you're a long-ball slugger."

Zeke shortened his grip on the bat for the first pitch, guided a soft bunt down the first base line. The contact of wood against the ball felt good.

It felt better and better when two solidly hit drives went into left field and one into left center. Then he got too far under a pitch and lofted an easy pop fly to shortstop. Four more drives that were in base-hit territory sped off his bat. A fear that Naffing had been too optimistic in referring to the batting slump he was "coming out of" faded from Zeke's thoughts.

Nobody shoved him, no player threw his weight around as Bull Manley had done at West Palm Beach so long ago. Long ago? Zeke chuckled. This was August. He had joined the Instructional League West Palm Beach Braves the previous October.

Not even a year ago—and here he was taking batting practice before a major league game on the roster of a major league ballclub!

When he left the batting cage, Zeke was facing the visitor's third base dugout. He was surprised to see three players in the gray traveling uniforms of the St. Louis Cardinals sitting on their bench and intently watching the Atlanta Braves who came to the plate. He recognized one of the trio as a catcher for the Cardinals in the Instructional League.

It stuck in his mind.

After the batting cage had been wheeled away, both teams had taken infield workouts, and the ground crew was readying the infield for play, Zeke remarked to Bob Naffing on the Cardinals watching Braves batting.

"Smart." Naffing nodded. "We have no monopoly on baseball brains. They're doing what you and I are going to be doing at every opportunity—getting stuff for their books on hitters. That catcher you recognized is a rookie brought up by the Cardinals from a farm club. He has to learn the hitters, and he probably won't catch many innings. So he's grabbing the chance to study hitters of other clubs while they take batting practice."

Naffing sat beside Zeke at the far end of the dugout bench when the game started. Not only Cardinal hitters, but men who came to the plate for the Braves fell under Naffing's critical eye. He talked about the strategy employed by the Cardinal manager on hit-and-run situations, steal situations; how various batters reacted when mates were on base. What did they do when the count was two-and-two? Three-and-two? Three-and-one? Did they go for the "cripple," or did they have a good enough batting eye to wait and force the pitcher to come in with a good pitch before they swung?

"You hear a lot about pitchers having a book on hitters," Naffing said. "And that's fine. Smart pitchers surely do. But in my opinion, it's *more* important for a catcher to have a book on every batter. He has to call pitches, no matter what chucker is on the mound."

Zeke Pender was very humble before half the game had been played. He began to appreciate the casual observation Skipper had made about never stopping learning.

Mike Oldham had given him plenty of advice, but Zeke recognized that Mike was not in the same league with Naffing when it came to painstaking and minute detail!

The Braves could not solve the output of the Cardinal southpaw—for seven innings. St. Louis batters put together two hits, a walk, and a sacrifice for a pair of runs in their seventh. They hit the Atlanta pitcher hard in the top of the eighth. Only a sensational stop of a wicked drive barely inside third base and an unbelievable throw nipped a man at first base to shut off one and possibly two runs.

In the bottom of the inning, the leadoff batter for the Braves beat out a hit to deep short. A strikeout, then a walk, and a fly to right moved runners to third and second, but two were out and the pitcher scheduled to bat.

"Pender!" His name from Skipper startled Zeke. "Grab a bat." Skipper made a gesture to the plate umpire and shouted something. Then he added to Zeke, "You're pinch hitting. You've got the green light to pick your pitch, but make him get it in there before you cut!"

Zeke stood outside the batter's box while the public address announced his name and number. He forced himself to relax when he stepped into the box and faced the pitcher.

The lefthander might try to slip a strike past and put him in the hole. He might try to get a rookie to go after a bad one. Zeke was ready.

He knew when the first pitch left the southpaw's hand that it was not for him. The umpire ruled it ball one. Zeke liked the second pitch, but when his bat met the spinning ball, Zeke knew he had misjudged the speed and was too far out in front. The crowd's rising ah-h-h died when the drive went into the stands fifteen feet foul.

Now the veteran Cardinal lefthander worked on the rookie. The count went to three-and-two. Zeke Pender fouled off five straight pitches, any one of which might have been ruled a third strike if he had let it go.

"Ducks on the pond! . . . Big one here and another at the pickup station! . . . Make him get it in there, kid, then clobber it!"

Encouragement came from coaches at third and first. Zeke kept his concentration on the pitcher. *Southpaw's curves break toward right-hand hitters. Medium fast ball inside.* Things clicked in Zeke's thoughts faster than he could have said them. But at the last instant the ball broke sharply *away* from him. It crossed the plate well inside the strike zone.

"Str-r-r-r-i-i-i-ke three!"

Zeke did not need the umpire's emphatic call to know he'd been had. He went to the dougout and slumped to the bench as the Braves took their gloves and trotted onto the field.

A strikeout his first big league time at bat. A base hit would have scored the tying runs. Zeke felt miserable. Naffing put a hand on the rookie's knee.

Naffing said, "You're in pretty good company. A lot of fine hitters have gone down because they were fooled by that screwball."

Zeke said nothing. "Any time a pinch hitter delivers," Naffing went on, "a manager is pleased, but I don't think Skipper is too disappointed with you."

"Don't try to con me! I struck out!"

"And you made the chucker throw eleven hard pitches. This guy sometimes weakens in late innings. If he comes back in the ninth, we may murder him good. Skipper figures the angles. He knows the Cards have a tired bullpen. The only reliever they have halfway ready happens to be a guy we hit like we own him.

You running the string out on their wronghander, using him up, just might mean the ballgame for us."

Tom Bary came from the Braves bullpen. The veteran righthander set down Cardinal batters in order in the top of the ninth. Then in the bottom of the inning, Naffing's thinking was borne out as though he could see into the future.

The Cardinal southpaw returned to the mound. He walked the first batter, got into a two-nothing hole on the second man to face him, and the Cardinal manager came from the dugout making a sign for a relief pitcher as he walked to the mound.

It was the hurler Naffing had said the Braves "hit like we own him."

Three solid base hits, a fielder's choice, a walk, and a grand slam home run put a numeral six on the scoreboard for the Braves with only one out. Braves, 6; Cardinals, 2.

The St. Louis club turned the tables in the second of the three-game series. A fine crowd that almost filled the Stadium to capacity on a Friday night saw the Braves' hitters handcuffed with only three scattered singles. One mistake by the Atlanta pitcher cost the game. He "hung" a high curve, and the Cardinal batter hammered the ball into the club deck ten feet inside the right foul marker.

Zeke was agreeably surprised to find Dennis Murphy sitting on the seat of his locker when he came into the clubhouse.

"Just about burned up the convertible trying to make it here in time for the whole game," Murphy said. "I figured you'd be catching. Well, now that Murphy's up here, I'll insist on you being behind the dish when they start me!"

"Which just might be about fourteen hours from now." Bob Naffing stood behind Zeke. He extended a hand to the rookie southpaw, "welcome," Naffing said. "Skipper picks the pitchers, of course, but reports from Austin are that you last worked down there three nights ago. You're ready, if Skip decides to work you tomorrow?"

"Ready, willing, and able." Dennis Murphy grinned. "One thing six wins at Austin gave me is confidence!"

Zeke Pender wholeheartedly believed that Dennis Murphy was ready when he warmed him up Saturday afternoon. He wished that the other part of Murphy's declaration—that he would insist on Zeke Pender behind the plate—would prove equally valid. But Skipper would be better off with Danberro. Murphy would be pitching to hitters he had never faced, and Danberro would know them all.

The battery for Atlanta was announced as Murphy, pitching; Pender, catching. Bob Naffing spoke to Zeke in a low tone while the Braves crowded to the dugout lip awaiting the signal to run out on the field.

"You've watched these guys a couple of games," Naffing said. "You have some idea what they hit and what they don't. Nobody expects you to call a no-hit game. Use your noodle and remember that every pitcher has one pet pitch—what he considers his get-'em-out-pitch. If Murphy gets in a jam, rely on that pitch, because he'll have more confidence in it."

Dennis Murphy was a long way from duplicating the no-hitter that had won the first-half title for the

West Palm Beach Braves and earned him promotion to Austin. Neither did Zeke Pender call every pitch perfectly. But the rookie battery was fortunate in having Braves power at the plate explode. Enjoying an 8-3 bulge going into the eighth inning, Dennis Murphy did not appear to be disturbed when Cardinal hitters battered his stuff for three runs. The Braves added two runs in their half of the inning. Braves, 10; Cardinals, 6.

The Cardinals scored two in the top of the ninth after two were out. A 10-8 ballgame. Skipper was out at the dugout lip. Activity in the right field bullpen became suddenly more intense. Zeke called time and went out to the mound. He wasted no words.

"You've got a great chance to go into the record book with a complete-game win for your first big league start," he told Murphy. "But you won't be here to finish if you keep monkeying around. Get with it!"

"What do you mean, monkeying around? There are two out. I can get another one whenever I want. I've been trying a new slow-slider that I've been working on."

"And you've been shaking me around after I've signed for pitches," Zeke said. "Okay, so you gained confidence at Austin—this is Atlanta, the big time! Did you ever consider how many runs are scored in major league ballgames after two outs? I've been studying these hitters. I know what pitchers have been getting them out on. You shake me off on this next guy—and I'll be right out here with the ball and *jam* it down your throat!"

Murphy got the batter on a popup off a change-up.

In the clubhouse, Skipper allowed sportswriters to interview his rookie battery. One of the newspapermen asked Murphy if he thought the good fortune he had experienced in his initial major league start would last. Dennis Murphy flashed a glance at Skipper, then at Bob Naffing, then at Zeke. A wide grin split his face.

"It may not last," he said, "but it's sure great while it does!"

15 : Catchers Have Troubles

THE ATLANTA BRAVES took to the road after the Cardinal series. Zeke sat in the visitor's dugout in Cincinnati and studied Red batters during batting practice. He studied them for three games. Danberro caught every inning. Zeke knew that the veteran would be behind the plate as often as Skipper felt he could help the ballclub more than another catcher.

Dennis Murphy was announced as starting pitcher for the opening game at Houston. While he warmed up Murphy, Zeke became aware that his roommate was not at top form.

Murphy never got anybody out in that game.

"I haven't got it." Dennis slammed the ball into the pocket of his glove when Zeke came to the mound after the first three Astro batters had hit safely. "All this stuff about pitchers always being confident they can get the other guys out is baloney. I know as well as you do that my fast one isn't hopping, I don't have control of my curve, my slider's more apt to slide out of your reach than fool a hitter, and I wouldn't dare try a change-up after I'd shown it to a batter once!"

Zeke nodded. "Slow things down as much as you can," he said. "Give bullpen pitchers as much time as possible."

He walked slowly back to the plate. He gave a sign to the Atlanta dugout on the way. Two pitchers in the Braves bullpen began throwing harder.

Murphy stalled, drew a sharp reprimand from the plate umpire, finally walked the batter. One Astro run counted, bases full. The pitcher who had given Zeke a bad time weeks ago in the B-Club-Miami U. game was brought in.

Zeke took the range-finding pitches, walked toward the mound. It was customary for a new pitcher and the catcher to check signs. The Braves reliever showed right off that his opinion of Zeke Pender had not changed. He held out his glove while Zeke was three yards from the mound.

"The ball, that's all I want from you," he said. "One finger for my fast one, two for my curve, three for a slider and four for a change-up. You sign and I'll decide what to throw!"

Zeke eyed him, words crowding to the tip of his tongue. Then he thought, *this guy has saved nine ballgames and been the pitcher of record in five other winning jobs since they put him in the bullpen. Sing small, Pender!*

He shrugged, tossed the ball, and returned to his position.

Houston scored three runs before the relief pitcher got them out. He had shaken off five pitches that Zeke signed for. In the dugout, Naffing caught Zeke's eye as the rookie shucked off his chest protector. Naffing held Zeke's gaze a moment, then shook his head.

The Braves did not score in their second inning. Then Astro hitters took up where they had left off in the first inning on Atlanta pitching. Two straight hits, and Skipper came to the mound. He flashed a glance at Zeke as the rookie catcher drew near, then talked to the pitcher.

"You're coming in there a little high, try sticking 'em up there lower. Get this guy to hit a grounder and we'll make the double play. You can work out of this." Then Skipper surprised Zeke. "How's his stuff, Pender?"

Zeke saw the pitcher's scowl. The rookie said slowly, "His curve's breaking sharp, and the slider's coming in there."

Skipper seemed to be waiting for more, finally nodded. "It's up to you to stop 'em," he told the pitcher. "We can't afford to leave any chucker in when the other guys are making runs too easy."

The Astros added two more runs to their total that inning. Danberro warmed up Tom Bary in the bullpen while the Braves batted in the third. Skipper said nothing, Naffing said nothing, nobody even glanced toward Zeke when Danberro and Bary were announced as the Atlanta battery for the bottom of the third inning.

Zeke crowded into the corner of the dugout and

wished he could crawl under the bench. The fact that Naffing did not come and sit beside him cut more deeply than having been taken from the game because Skipper felt he was not doing his job.

Tom Bary turned back the Astro attack. He was lifted in the eighth for a pinch hitter and the move backfired. The man batting for him bounced into a double play; the pitcher who came in for Bary was shelled for six hits and four runs. Nothing made Zeke feel any better. He was silent and morose when he and Murphy reached their hotel room.

"Okay, so I'll take some of the blame!" Murphy sunk his fist in a pillow: "I couldn't have beaten a Little League team tonight and I dragged you down with—no, I didn't!"

He turned and faced his roommate, went on. "You told me back in Waycross to grow up. Now I'm saying you're the one who needs to grow up! You've got to get over the kid-awe-inferiority that eats in you. You're a big league catcher, so *be* big league. If you'd shaped up that hotshot, bullpen-fireman, you'd never have been lifted from the ballgame!"

The Braves dropped two of three games at Houston. They moved on to Los Angeles to tangle with the Dodgers. Bob Naffing sat with Zeke and checked batters during batting practice and the first game. It was a tight battle all the way. Going into the ninth inning, the score was a 1-1 tie.

A single by the Braves leadoff man set up an obvious bunt situation. First baseman and third baseman came in on the grass. The Dodger pitcher threw a waste ball, high and away, while third baseman and first baseman charged in. A pickoff play was in the works, but the Braves baserunner was alert and easily beat the catcher's snap throw to the second baseman, covering first. Ball one on the batter.

"Watch this one, Zeke," Naffing said. "You may see why Skipper's one of the really good managers. He never hesitates to deviate from percentage if the gamble warrants.

"They know that our fastest man's on first. They know he may break for second. This Dodger catcher may waste another pitch on the chance he might be going."

The baserunner did not go. The pitchout made the count two-and-oh.

"Now, they're in a quandary," Naffing said. "They know that Skipper sometimes hangs out the hit-and-run sign in this situation. A catcher must catalogue clubs and combinations and take a lot of things into consideration. This is not a spot for a pitchout."

It was not a pitchout. A bunt was fouled, then a curve clipped a corner. Two-and-two.

"Another tough spot for their catcher. If he calls a pitchout, he may trap the baserunner—if Dan goes. But if Dan doesn't go, their pitcher is in a hole and the catcher is responsible for having him there.

"Always try to keep from giving the offensive team any edge. A pitchout on a two-and-two count puts your pitcher in a three-and-two spot that is *not* advantageous and changes your pitching strategy. We'll see what the Dodger catcher does."

He did not call for a pitchout. The baserunner took off with the pitcher's delivery, and the batter hit behind the runner through the hole left when the second baseman dashed to cover the bag. The perfectly

RUSH

executed run-and-hit play put Braves on first and third. A long fly to left center scored one run, then a booming drive to the right field corner was good for three bases and a second run over the plate. At the end of the game the 2 in the top of the ninth frame on the scoreboard was the only figure other than zeroes.

Zeke Pender brought Naffing's analysis of attack and battery strategy to Dennis Murphy's attention in their room after the game. The rookie lefthander regarded his roommate a long moment.

"Yeah." Murphy nodded. "Real inside stuff. Naffing and Mike Oldham and other coaches have crammed you full, but you know something? The only guy who can really do you any good is Zeke Pender."

"Sure. A fellow has to *do* the things coaches point out."

"It's more than just doing, at least just performing things mechanically. I'm no old-head, but I know I'm right. Just ask Naffing!"

Zeke did not have to ask Naffing. The former Braves catcher came to him in the clubhouse before the game.

"Danberro may have pulled a muscle yesterday in diving to make that tag in the eighth. He's going to start, but Skipper warned him not to try to go on if his leg bothered. The chances are you'll get a call to work the final two or three innings in any case."

Naffing regarded Zeke a moment, then went on. "You're not stupid," he said, "but you have a mental block of fixation or whatever a headshrinker would term it—I mean the way you let some of the pitchers push you around. Get this and never forget it: The catcher has to have respect and trust from his pitchers, but he also has to be boss out there. He may not be a holler guy but he has to be a take-charge guy one way or another. If a pitcher is shaking you around, and you're sure the sign you gave is for the right pitch for the situation and the hitter at the plate, you just keep giving the same sign. If the pitcher is stubborn, you go out there and lay things right on the line.

"Catchers have several kinds of troubles, Zeke, but the thing that's holding you back is lack of aggressiveness with your pitchers. Keep in mind that in the Braves organization, primary responsibility for keeping a team firing on all cylinders rests on the catcher."

16 : Big League Backstop

BRAVES BATTERS found Dodger pitching to their liking that day. A two-run second inning was followed by a four-run rally in the fourth that sent the starting Los Angeles pitcher to the showers.

They added another pair of runs in the sixth inning after the Dodgers had broken the ice with a single marker in their fifth. Enjoying an 8-1 margin, the Braves pitcher seemed to have the game under control. That no baseball game can ever be considered completely under control until the final out is made was proved again in that game.

The pitcher suddenly lost his stuff. He began pressing and became "wild down the middle," in baseball parlance. Four hits boomed off Dodger bats. Two walks and a scratch hit off a relief pitcher left the bases full and a 4 on the board in the Los Angeles seventh inning.

"Neither one was getting the corners," Naffing said after the inning was over. "They were laying pitches up there too fat."

Skipper must have agreed with Naffing. He went to the mound next inning when the first batter rapped a long drive to right that was barely foul as it left the ballpark. Skipper talked briefly with the pitcher, then signaled the bullpen for relief.

Tom Bary came to the mound. He walked the batter and two infield outs chased him to third. Then Bary threw a curve wide into the dirt. Danberro lunged for the wild pitch, chased it to the wall, but the run scored. Danberro limped perceptibly going back to his position. Time was called, and the Braves trainer ran to the catcher.

"Pender!" Skipper barked the name. "Get your gear on, you're catching!"

Bob Naffing spoke rapidly to the rookie. "Be aggressive. Take charge!"

Zeke settled behind the batter. His mental book on the man at the plate was: good fast-ball hitter. Doesn't do much with slow-breaking stuff. He signed for a slow curve. Tom Bary shook him off. Zeke signed for a slider.

Bary's delivery did not look right to Zeke. The pitch was high and hung. Fortunately the batter took it. Zeke called time and ran out to the mound.

"Your rhythm is off," he told the veteran pitcher. "You pushed that one up there, and there wasn't a thing on it. Loosen up!"

Bary stared, started to say something, and Zeke looked him steadily in the eye.

"You shook me off last fall in an Instructional League game," Zeke said. "Three times—and you lost the ballgame. You told me afterward you couldn't stand alibis. Okay, be bullheaded now, and see who needs to come up with alibis!"

Zeke was trembling as he turned and stalked back to the plate. He wasn't sure whether he trembled from anger or from shock at the temerity he had shown in bawling out a major league pitcher. He signed for the same pitch and Bary toed the rubber and delivered a good slow slider. The batter rolled it weakly back to the mound.

The veteran pitcher closed the door on Dodger hitters. The game ended with the scoureboard showing an 8-6 win for Atlanta.

In the clubhouse, Tom Bary came over to Zeke's locker. Bary held out his hand. "Your tip was a good one," Bary said. "I think getting careless and dropping into an old pitching fault contributed to my arm trouble. Thanks for jerking me up, kid."

Skipper picked Dennis Murphy to start the final game of the Los Angles series.

"Smart move," Murphy said to Zeke. "He figures I may come up with a decent game and you won't have to battle some other chucker. A win today will do us both some good, Zeke."

Murphy was sharp. He breezed along for five innings, then a call of the umpire on a three-and-one pitch irked the southpaw. He yelled, "What was the matter with that one!"

The umpire did not reply verbally, only made the

classic move by dusting off the plate with his little broom. Zeke fired the ball back hard. He signed for a fast ball. Murphy wriggled his glove. Zeke signed for a fast curve. The pitch was close to the strike zone, but outside. Zeke knew that Murphy had no legitimate beef.

But Dennis Murphy started belligerently toward the plate. Zeke called time, trotted toward the irate pitcher. He said grimly, "I'm taking your advice. I'm boss-man out here, get that!"

"And you'll turn me over your knee and whack me good!" Murphy spoke quickly. "Way to go!" Murphy grinned. "Yessir, Mr. Pender, that's how you handle a stupid pitcher when he gets out of line!"

The Braves came into San Francisco to meet a hot Giants club. Luis Danberro's pulled muscle was not responding rapidly to treatment, and Zeke Pender was the Braves' catcher.

Both clubs hammered the opposing pitching. The Braves starter lasted one and two-thirds innings. His earned-run average would suffer when the six runs the Giants tallied were counted.

The Braves caught up in the third inning. From that point on, it was a seesaw 7-6, then 8-7, then 9-8 game. The Giants were on the short end, with baserunners on third and second and two out, when a burly figure came from the San Francisco dugout.

"Manley, Number 16, hitting for Jones," the public address announced.

Manley stooped and scooped a handful of dirt before he stepped into the batter's box. He rubbed the dirt on his bat and said sneeringly to Zeke, "Well, the grapevine has it that you're ticketed back to the sticks. The Braves' brass know now what a mistake they made in letting me get away. Make a wrong guess on how this rinky-dink out there pitches to me, and you'll read in the papers about their closing the deal to bring me back to the Braves!"

Something stuck in Zeke's mind. He suddenly recalled words of Bob Naffing's at Mr. Murphy's in Juno Beach. *He has weaknesses at bat and more behind the plate.*

Flashes of pictures featuring Bull Manley skipped through Zeke's mind in kaleidoscopic pattern. Abruptly, he was as sure as he could be that he knew the weakness Naffing had spotted in Manley as a batter. Bull Manley was a "guess" hitter. When he happened to guess correctly and was set for a pitch, he walloped the ball.

But hitters who tried to guess what pitch was coming played right into the hands of smart catchers and pitchers.

"He'd be figuring a breaking ball, not a hittable pitch." Zeke spoke as though talking to himself. "Well, guess hitters can be crossed up. We'll feed him a fast one right down the middle!"

Zeke was aware of the quick glance Manley threw him. He saw the smirk on Manley's face. He felt confident that Manley was figuring that it would be a breaking ball, out of the strike zone.

This was a dirty trick to pull, but what was that thing Mike Oldham said? Dog-eat-dog in pro ball. Zeke signed for a fast ball.

The pitcher wiggled his glove to signify he

wanted another sign. Zeke groaned. He had overlooked the fact that the pitcher was the man who had been expected to be a starter and had given him a bad time before. Zeke's jaw hardened.

He crouched and repeated the sign for a fast ball. The pitcher shook him off. A third time Zeke made the signal for a fast ball, and again the pitcher's glove wiggled.

"Quit stalling, Pender," the umpire said. "Pitch to him or put him on!"

Zeke said, "Time!"

He started for the mound. He was surprised to see from the edge of his vision that Skipper had left the dugout. The manager of the Braves was not walking slowly. He came on with purposeful stride. Zeke spoke hurriedly before Skipper got there.

"I know this guy. I want a fast ball," Zeke said. "I'll take responsibility. If you don't want to pitch what I call, then let's have the p.a. announce that *you're* calling *all* pitches—in case you get clobbered."

"And clobbered you may be, in more ways than one." Skipper had quite evidently heard the last part of Zeke's ultimatum. Oddly, Zeke found himself thinking of what Naffing had told Mr. Murphy most often went on at mound conferences. This one was different. "I've been waiting for you to take charge, Pender," Skipper said. He held the pitcher's eyes. "You accept that Pender *is* in charge—or get out of the ballgame. That's the choice you have!"

The pitcher looked sullen, shrugged, nodded. Zeke felt abruptly hollow inside, but he did not let Manley see any sign of being perturbed. Crouched back of the plate, Zeke muttered, but distinctly enough for Manley to hear, "No change. Here comes the fire-ball!"

"Who you trying to con, Busher?" Manley sneered. "I've got you figured now!"

He made no offer at the perfect strike.

Zeke said, "Now he'll guess a change-up. We'll cross him with another fast one."

Manley snorted, wriggled his spikes in the dirt. Zeke wondered if he might have outsmarted himself. But again Manley did not offer at a good fast ball.

"Three times in a row." Zeke mumbled as he crouched. He signed for a half-speed curve.

Bull Manley looked far from a hitter clubs would be fighting over as he offered weakly and too late at a curve breaking in across the plate.

The pitcher said nothing to Zeke as they went to the dugout. Skipper said, "Nice going out there. That's the way a winning battery works."

After the game—a 9-8 win for the Braves—Skipper parried questions of sportswriters in the club-house. He raised his voice a little at one question and looked across at Zeke Pender.

"I wouldn't go so far as to say we won't miss Dan-berro, if his injury doesn't respond to treatment," the Braves manager said. "Any club misses steadiness and clutch hitting. But let me make it clear—we have a big league backstop filling in, and he'll get better as he gains experience!"

Appendix

All major league baseball clubs provide every aid they can to help the development of their young ballplayers. The manager and coaching staff of the Atlanta Braves constantly revise and add to their written aid material for every player.

The following *Instructions for Catchers* is authentic material provided for all candidates for the position of catcher in the Braves training camps. It was given to the author by Mr. James Fanning, a former major league catcher who has served the Braves as farm-team manager, scout, special assignment man, and assistant general manager.

INSTRUCTIONS FOR CATCHERS

Position

The ideal position for a catcher's feet is to have the left foot extended in front of the right by a matter of inches—not to exceed six. This position provides the catcher with more flexibility in moving, not only to the right but in all directions.

When the catcher assumes the position of catching after coming out of the sign-giving crouch, there is one very important point to remember: *every movement made must be the same for every pitch.* It is surprising how many catchers—even some major leaguers—develop faulty habits that will tip off pitches to the opponents.

There are two ways of making this important matter a habit. *First:* jump from the crouch into a catching position. *Second:* assume the catching position on a very definite count. For example, at the count of "one" move the left foot into position. At the count of "two" move the right foot into position. At the count of "three" assume the catcher's position.

There are pitchers who have types of balls that will prove troublesome to some catchers. For example, a sidearm sinker ball pitcher who throws a ball occasionally to the right side of the catcher may be a troublesome man to catch. The simplest way of handling this problem is to shift the weight on your feet to protect yourself against that one pitch.

You must be careful in the shift of this weight not to tip off any pitches to the opposition. This is merely a protective measure to make your receiving of more benefit to the pitcher.

The Target

Now, having assumed the position of catching, with the left foot in front of the right, and having bent to catch, the one most important feature remaining is to be sure that your pitcher—when looking in—sees a target squarely facing him.

The comfort angle in catching is a personal angle; the target angle in catching is for the benefit of your pitcher. A catcher should always keep in mind that he is an instrument of the pitcher. Everything the catcher does should be to aid the efficiency of the pitcher.

A catcher must always be sure that whenever he is giving a pitcher a target with his glove, he does not move that glove until the pitcher has released the ball. There is nothing more disconcerting to the pitcher than to be given a target and then, just when he needs it most as he is letting the ball go, to have it move.

Shifting

Practice of short, quick side steps will help any catcher develop his ability to shift. On a dance floor, in a gym, while walking on the street (you may be thought "kookie" by passersby, but what catcher cares?) or in your own room, practice in the quick side step will pay off. The shift is practiced whenever possible by assuming a catcher's position—moving the left foot to the right and stepping to the side with the right. It should be practiced to the left, to the right, forward, or sideways, switching the foot that is used first to correspond to the direction in which one is going.

Throwing

A catcher should never throw a ball as hard as he can to any base. His chief concern should always be to get the ball away as fast as is humanly possible and with a sufficient amount of speed to carry to the thrown base. The ball ought to be easily handled by the infielder. A catcher should not try to show how hard he can throw.

In throwing back to the pitcher the catcher guides the ball as closely to the left shoulder of the pitcher as it is possible to do. Conserve the energy of the pitcher, don't make him reach for the ball. The throw to lefthanders is opposite, of course. The young catcher should practice throwing at the gloved-hand shoulder of a pitcher with some force behind the ball.

When the catcher is going to throw to second base, he will throw at exactly the same spot he has been accustomed to throwing, but he will add a little more effort to the throw, and he will find that the ball will carry to second base. The importance of having this in mind is to realize that a throw to second base is merely a throw to the pitcher, but with more on the ball than is used normally.

Throwing accuracy comes with practice. Every catcher should practice throwing at a moving object. For example, have a baseman run toward an unprotected base and throw the ball to that base so it will arrive with the fielder, high enough for him to handle the throw and make the tag. A very fine practice for any catcher is to practice throwing at an unoccupied base.

If your throwing is off, check first to see that your balance is on the back foot. Secondly, check to see if your forward stride with the guide foot is normal—straight ahead. A most important single factor in successful throwing is throwing overhand so that vertical spin results in straight throws. Thus, a ball will not sink or "tail" off to the right and be difficult to catch, but will go straight on a line.

Receiving

Upon receiving the ball there should be no movement of the glove to influence the umpire in his decision except whatever movement is necessary to start the mechanics of taking the ball out of the glove in order to swing into the position of throwing.

The first consideration of any young catcher should be to take the ball immediately in his bare hand and bring the ball into a throwing position. This is a habit that when developed will save untold stolen bases and will assist in the development of a catcher, because he is always in a position to throw. His actions will keep baserunners from taking undue liberties. While the catcher is in position to throw, the opposition will have little opportunity to practice deception. Catchers must practice and practice and practice getting rid of the ball as fast as possible, with greater regard for accuracy than for speed of flight.

A low ball is always caught up—a high ball is always caught down. Every ball should be caught in a strike zone if it is possible. For example, a curve ball that might have been low could very well be called a strike if a catcher reached out and caught it in a strike zone, rather than waiting for the ball to complete its full arc of curve.

Foul Flies and Bunts

When a catcher throws off his mask to catch a foul fly, the first thing he must do is get under the ball as fast as he can. His second thought is to catch the foul fly "on the tip of his nose." It is much easier to take a half step backward than it is a half step forward. If he starts to whirl and becomes confused, he should look immediately towards the ground, until he has focused his eyes on the ground, then look up, and his whirling will stop. The element of time is not to be considered. One does not whirl on a foul tip if it is not very high in the air.

A catcher fielding a bunt should never face away from the base to which he is going to make a play. It is very important that in the fielding of a bunt a catcher should attempt to scoop the ball into the mitt with the bare hand, rather than attempt to pick up the ball without the aid of his mitt. This habit will offset many fielding errors during the course of a season.

On all bunts, the catcher is the man who is in complete charge of directing the throw. He should yell with authority to the fielder and tell him to which base the throw must be made. Decisions on plays like this are matters of judgment and experience. The most important consideration is the prejudging of the baserunner's speed, before the ball is bunted, and the complete knowledge of the agility of the pitcher or fielder who is fielding the ball. A comparison of the two, when the play presents itself, will be the determining factor in your decision. Right or wrong, you must be firm in your decision and must yell loud enough for the fielder to hear you.

The Pitchout

In professional baseball, a catcher should use the pitchout purely as a measure for the benefit of his team. He uses it for defensive purposes when he has definite knowledge that the runner is going to try to steal. He uses it to upset the running style of his opponents—for example, when a catcher is playing against a team that uses the hit-and-run quite frequently, or is known as a base-stealing ball club.

The first couple of opportunities he has to call for a pitchout, where the pitchout will not hurt his pitcher's effectiveness, he should do so to influence the thinking of the opposition. He will raise a question in their minds for the entire game as to whether he is going to pitchout or not. The question in their minds may be sufficiently strong to delay that ball club from using its usual tactics and therefore force them to play an unnatural type of game. It is common to pitchout in squeeze bunt situations.

A Catcher's Job

The first consideration of a catcher is to catch a winning game and to help the pitcher in every way possible. Remember that the pitcher is the one who is supposed to look good, not the catcher.

It is much more important to the success of a baseball team—and particularly to a pitcher—that the catcher know the strength and weakness of his pitcher, rather than the strength and weaknesses of the opposition. If you know your pitcher and know what he can do and insist that he do his best with his best, then the odds are going to be in your favor.

Your spirit and determination will be a determining factor in the way your pitcher feels in facing the different issues during the course of a game. Remember that the entire baseball field is before you, and you alone are in front of him. From your actions the pitcher will get the feeling of the fellows who he cannot see. The inspiration you give to a pitcher cannot be overemphasized. Remember that your pitcher and the entire baseball team is looking at you on every pitch. Your actions can either key a ball club up to its desired pitch or let it down. You will be the determining factor in a great percentage of games, as far as the spirit and hustle of a ball club is concerned. Remember that you are an assistant of the pitcher and that your job is to be just that: to assist the pitcher. You, above everyone else, with the exception of the manager, must always have a very confident attitude, because a game is over only when there are three men out in the ninth inning for the opposition.

A Catcher Helps

A very good practice for catchers to develop is the matter of assisting the pitcher as he is about to release the ball. A pitcher who has a tendency to hang a curve ball may be helped by having the catcher shift his weight, just as the pitcher is about to release the ball. This shift of weight will make the pitcher realize that the ball must be thrown with the catcher's shift to his new position, and will give him a tendency to hang onto the ball long enough to correct the fault that he has of hanging the curve ball.

Along these lines, if a catcher realizes that his pitcher is having difficulty controlling his low pitch and it is costing him strikes, then the catcher will catch from a higher position than he would normally, to help correct the pitcher's trouble.

Young pitchers and very old pitchers often pitch to the hitter, instead of to the catcher. If a pitcher you are catching tends to make this pitching error, it is not too difficult to detect. By merely shifting your position behind the plate, you will know within a couple of pitches that the pitcher is not shifting with you and therefore must be pitching to the hitter.

Any pitcher who pitches to the hitter is entirely at the mercy of the hitter's batting stance. For example, a pitcher who is trying to pitch inside to a batter will continue to pitch inside to the batter even though he steps away from the plate. Before he realizes it, the pitcher will be pitching with the count "two balls and no strikes" every time that hitter comes to bat. It is then a simple matter for the hitter to shift his stance for the next thrown strike, or to accept the inevitable base on balls—if the pitcher does not correct the fault.

The problem of protecting home plate against the runner who is attempting to score is simple. Your job is to get the ball and tag the runner. Do your job. It is foolish, and against the rules, for any catcher to attempt to block the plate unless the throw carries the catcher into the runner's path—and then he is not blocking the plate.

If it is a question of the runner or the ball—if you don't have the ball, the man is safe—so get the ball!

The distinguishing mark between a catcher and a great receiver is his ability to catch low balls, particularly balls in the dirt and to save strikes for his pitcher by catching every pitch in a strike zone.

Stolen Bases

On any attempted steal, a catcher should realize before the play comes up how fast the base runner is who is trying to steal. Then, when the pitch is made, he will see how much of a jump the runner has. He will know how much time he has to get rid of the ball in order to throw the runner out.

Catchers should constantly remind their pitchers not to be careless in holding a man on. This continual reminder may save a ball game that might easily have been lost because a steal put a runner in position to score. There will be times when your infielders will not get the proper break to second base, and your throw must meet them someplace between their position and the bag. When this happens, the practice that you have gone through in throwing to a moving target will be invaluable.

Get rid of the ball as fast as you can, as accurately as you can, and you won't have to worry about how hard you throw. It will not do your club any good if you throw the ball so hard that a moving infielder can't handle it for the tag.

With men on first and third bases, and a possibility of an attempted steal, it is the catcher's duty to figure out his play. His judgment will be influenced by the score, the type of runners, and the type of opposition. However, in professional baseball, the manager will usually direct this play by use of a sign to the catcher. The catcher in turn informs the pitcher, shortstop, second baseman, and third baseman of the strategy—again by a sign. The ability of your pitcher to hold the man on base is going to be an important consideration in all plays of this type, along with the existing score of the ball game.

If your manager doesn't control the strategy in the man-on-first-and-third situation, a catcher's thinking goes along these lines: tie score, two out in the ninth—no reason for a catcher to throw to second base. The man going down is not your important consideration. Therefore, fake a throw to second and attempt to catch the man at third.

If the man on first is fast, and the man on third is slow—throw that ball through to second base as fast as you can get rid of it. You can handle the man at third.

Now, if the man at third is the fast man, and the man at first is slow, you fake the man back to third and then throw to second.

Perhaps most important of all to a catcher: never stop studying your pitchers and never miss an opportunity to help them and your team.

Report used by Atlanta Braves, similar to reports that were made on Zeke Pender.

INDIVIDUAL PLAYER REPORT

DATE OF REPORT SCOUT

NAME IN FULL

CLUB LEAGUE

HOME ADDRESS

POSITION AGE WGT. HGT. BATS THROWS

PHYSICAL DESCRIPTION

NATIONALITY MARRIED

HITTING POWER HABITS

RUNNING BASE RUNNING HUSTLE

FIELDING ATTITUDE ALERTNESS

ARM ACCURACY PROSPECT

PITCHERS { SPEED CHANGE POISE
CURVE CONTROL STAMINA

PLAYER'S STRENGTH

PLAYER'S WEAKNESS

PLAYER'S MILITARY STATUS

HOW MANY GAMES HAVE YOU SEEN HIM PLAY?

WHAT CLASSIFICATION CAN HE NOW PLAY?

HOW MANY YEARS BEFORE MAJOR LEAGUER?

DATE PLAYER GRADUATED(S)HIGH SCHOOL

ANY PREVIOUS PRO. EXPERIENCE?

PLAYER'S BASEBALL HISTORY AND REMARKS:

Card Is to Be Used in Reporting on ALL PLAYERS in Atlanta Organization and On PROSPECTS Only Outside the System